Childhood

OF FAMOUS AMERICANS

ATHLETES

BABE RUTH, *Van Riper, Jr.*
JIM THORPE, *Van Riper, Jr.*
KNUTE ROCKNE, *Van Riper, Jr.*
LOU GEHRIG, *Van Riper, Jr.*

AUTHORS and COMPOSERS

ERNIE PYLE, *Wilson*
FRANCIS SCOTT KEY, *Stevenson*
HARRIET BEECHER STOWE, *Widdemer*
JAMES FENIMORE COOPER, *Winders*
JAMES WHITCOMB RILEY, *Mitchell*
JOHN PHILIP SOUSA, *Weil*
KATE DOUGLAS WIGGIN, *Mason*
KATHARINE LEE BATES, *Myers*
LEW WALLACE, *Schaaf*
LOUISA ALCOTT, *Wagoner*
MARK TWAIN, *Mason*
MARY MAPES DODGE, *Mason*
NOAH WEBSTER, *Higgins*
STEPHEN FOSTER, *Higgins*
WASHINGTON IRVING, *Widdemer*

 ## BUSINESSMEN

ALLAN PINKERTON, *Borland and Speicher*
A. P. GIANNINI, *Hammontree*
JOHN JACOB ASTOR, *Anderson*
JOHN WANAMAKER, *Burt*
WALTER CHRYSLER, *Weddle*

EARLY SETTLERS

JAMES OGLETHORPE, *Parks*
MYLES STANDISH, *Stevenson*
PETER STUYVESANT, *Widdemer*
VIRGINIA DARE, *Stevenson*
WILLIAM BRADFORD, *Smith*
WILLIAM PENN, *Mason*

ENTERTAINERS

ANNIE OAKLEY, *Wilson*
LOTTA CRABTREE, *Place*
THE RINGLING BROTHERS, *Burt*
WILL ROGERS, *Van Riper, Jr.*

EXPLORERS and PIONEERS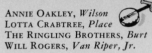

AMELIA EARHART, *Howe*
BUFFALO BILL, *Stevenson*
CARL BEN EIELSON, *Myers and Burnett*
DANIEL BOONE, *Stevenson*
DAVY CROCKETT, *Parks*
GEORGE ROGERS CLARK, *Wilkie*
JED SMITH, *Burt*
JIM BOWIE, *Winders*
JIM BRIDGER, *Winders*
JOHN SEVIER, *Steele*
KIT CARSON, *Stevenson*
MERIWETHER LEWIS, *Bebenroth*
NARCISSA WHITMAN, *Warner*
RICHARD BYRD, *Van Riper, Jr.*
ROBERT PEARY, *Clark*
SIMON KENTON, *Wilkie*
WILL CLARK, *Wilkie*
WILLIAM FARGO, *Wilkie*
ZEB PIKE, *Stevenson*

FOUNDERS OF OUR NATION

ALEC HAMILTON, *Higgins*
BEN FRANKLIN, *Stevenson*
DEWITT CLINTON, *Widdemer*
GEORGE WASHINGTON, *Stevenson*
JOHN QUINCY ADAMS, *Weil*
NATHAN HALE, *Stevenson*
PATRICK HENRY, *Barton*
PAUL REVERE, *Stevenson*
TOM JEFFERSON, *Monsell*

INDIANS

POCAHONTAS, *Seymour*
PONTIAC, *Peckham*
SACAGAWEA, *Seymour*
SEQUOYAH, *Snow*
SITTING BULL, *Stevenson*
SQUANTO, *Stevenson*
TECUMSEH, *Stevenson*

NAVAL HEROES

DAVID FARRAGUT, *Long*
GEORGE DEWEY, *Long*
JOHN PAUL JONES, *Snow*
MATTHEW CALBRAITH PERRY, *Scharbach*
OLIVER HAZARD PERRY, *Long*
RAPHAEL SEMMES, *Snow*
STEPHEN DECATUR, *Smith*

NOTED WIVES and MOTHERS

ABIGAIL ADAMS, *Wagoner*
DOLLY MADISON, *Monsell*
JESSIE FREMONT, *Wagoner*
MARTHA WASHINGTON, *Wagoner*
MARY TODD LINCOLN, *Wilkie*
NANCY HANKS, *Stevenson*
RACHEL JACKSON, *Govan*

SCIENTISTS and INVENTORS

ALBERT EINSTEIN, *Hammontree*
ALECK BELL, *Widdemer*
CYRUS McCORMICK, *Dobler*
ELIAS HOWE, *Corcoran*
ELI WHITNEY, *Snow*
ELIZABETH BLACKWELL, *Henry*
GEORGE CARVER, *Stevenson*
GEORGE EASTMAN, *Henry*
HENRY FORD, *Aird and Ruddiman*
JOHN AUDUBON, *Mason*
LUTHER BURBANK, *Burt*
MARIA MITCHELL, *Melin*
ROBERT FULTON, *Henry*
SAMUEL MORSE, *Snow*
TOM EDISON, *Guthridge*
WALTER REED, *Higgins*
WILBUR AND ORVILLE WRIGHT, *Stevenson*
WILL AND CHARLIE MAYO, *Hammontree*

SOCIAL and CIVIC LEADERS

BETSY ROSS, *Weil*
BOOKER T. WASHINGTON, *Stevenson*
CLARA BARTON, *Stevenson*
DAN BEARD, *Mason*
FRANCES WILLARD, *Mason*
JANE ADDAMS, *Wagoner*
JOHN L. LEWIS, *Korson*
J. STERLING MORTON, *Moore*
JULIA WARD HOWE, *Wagoner*
JULIETTE LOW, *Higgins*
LILIUOKALANI, *Newman*
LUCRETIA MOTT, *Burnett*
MOLLY PITCHER, *Stevenson*
OLIVER WENDELL HOLMES, JR., *Dunham*
SUSAN ANTHONY, *Monsell*

SOLDIERS

ANTHONY WAYNE, *Stevenson*
BEDFORD FORREST, *Parks*
DAN MORGAN, *Bryant*
ETHAN ALLEN, *Winders*
FRANCIS MARION, *Steele*
ISRAEL PUTNAM, *Stevenson*
JEB STUART, *Winders*
NATHANAEL GREENE, *Peckham*
ROBERT E. LEE, *Monsell*
SAM HOUSTON, *Stevenson*
TOM JACKSON, *Monsell*
U. S. GRANT, *Stevenson*
WILLIAM HENRY HARRISON, *Peckham*
ZACK TAYLOR, *Wilkie*

STATESMEN

ABE LINCOLN, *Stevenson*
ANDY JACKSON, *Stevenson*
DAN WEBSTER, *Smith*
FRANKLIN ROOSEVELT, *Weil*
HENRY CLAY, *Monsell*
JAMES MONROE, *Widdemer*
JEFF DAVIS, *de Grummond and Delaune*
JOHN MARSHALL, *Monsell*
TEDDY ROOSEVELT, *Parks*
WOODROW WILSON, *Monsell*

Israel Putnam

Fearless Boy

Illustrated by Jerry Robinson

Israel Putnam

Fearless Boy

By Augusta Stevenson

the NEW *Bobbs-Merrill* COMPANY, INC.
® AN ASSOCIATE OF HOWARD W. SAMS & CO., INC.
Publishers • INDIANAPOLIS • NEW YORK

Dedicated to Elmer William Stout,
an ardent student of American History

Illustrations

Contents

Books by Augusta Stevenson

★ Israel Putnam

Fearless Boy

On the Frontier

THE YOUNG boy in the big bed in the big attic was scared—so scared he couldn't sleep. And it wasn't because he heard wolves howling. He had heard them ever since he could remember.

He was born out here on the Massachusetts frontier on January 17, 1718. He had lived in this small frame house all of his life up to now, October, 1725. That would be seven-and-a-half years.

"I know why I'm frightened," Israel Putnam thought. "The wolves have always been in the forest before. Now they're in our clearing."

He started to get up. He was going to crawl

11

into his older brothers' bed. Then he stopped. "No, I won't. They'd tease me about it."

He drew the covers over his head and fell asleep.

The next morning he asked his sister, Huldah, if she had heard the wolves last night. Huldah was one year older than Israel, but she was just like him in one way. She didn't scare easily. She also had lived on the frontier all of her life.

"Did I hear them!" she exclaimed. "I couldn't sleep. I never heard such howling. It woke Mehitable, and she was so scared she cried. Then Mother let her sleep with her."

"Of course she was scared—she's only five. Do you think the pack was fighting?" asked Israel.

"Mother said they might be dancing."

"Wolves dancing!"

"Foxes do sometimes when it's moonlight. People have seen them," Huldah said.

"But foxes aren't fierce like wolves."

12

"Maybe moonlight changes them. And they howl when they don't get partners."

Israel laughed. "Maybe so," he agreed. "But I think they were fighting to see which one would become leader of the pack."

Now Mehitable called from the bedroom and Huldah went in to dress her.

One morning the two older boys got up earlier than usual. They were very quiet, for they didn't want to wake Israel.

But he heard them and sat up. "Why are you up so early?" he asked.

William answered, for he was the eldest and ran the farm. "We're going to begin a new clearing."

"Can't I help? I've used an ax before."

"Just on the woodpile. Dry wood is easier to cut than the green wood of a tree," said William.

"But I could cut off the smaller limbs."

"He's certainly strong enough," eighteen-year-old David put in. "I've never seen such arm muscles on a boy of his age."

"My hands are strong, too," Israel boasted.

"Well, you can try the small limbs," said the older brother.

Israel jumped out of bed. "I'll hurry."

"There's no hurry. We wouldn't be ready for you till afternoon. The first tree is huge."

Israel was disappointed. "I'd like to watch you work. I'd like to see you swing your axes."

"Oh, let him come now!" David exclaimed.

"All right, you may come, Israel. That is, if Mother doesn't object."

The three Putnams crept down the steep stairs. Their mother didn't hear them till they reached the kitchen. They went out into the lean-to to wash and comb. Then each boy took his place at the table. Israel and David sat on a bench at one side. William and Mrs. Putnam had stools.

Israel smiled when he saw the food. "Good!" he cried. "Hot hominy and cream! I like it."

They all did, from the way they ate. No one had time to talk. Mrs. Putnam filled their bowls again. She looked with pride at her husky sons.

Then she spoke. "Where will you make the new clearing, William?"

"We'd like to clear the hill back of the house, if you are willing."

"Indeed I am! I've always been afraid of that hill. It's a good hiding place for Indians. Your father wanted to clear it, but he was too busy with his cattle and sheep."

"He told me he did," William said. "That was shortly before he died. He said our house would make a good target here at the foot of the hill."

"There won't be any hiding places left when we get through," David boasted.

"Ha! Ha!" Israel laughed. "I'm going to help them, Mother—if you don't care."

"Will you keep him well away from falling trees, boys?"

"We'll warn him," William promised.

The woodcutters began at the bottom of the low hill. Israel understood the reason for this. "It's so the tree above can fall into a clear space. If they began at the top, there'd be a jumble."

He watched his brothers with pride. "I want

to swing an ax the way they do," he said to himself. "It's beautiful!"

After a time he decided to look about. So he began to climb the hill. When he reached the top, he looked down. Below were the valley and the narrow road that ended at the Putnam farm.

"If anyone takes this road, we'll know he's coming here," he said. "There's no other place to go."

Just now he was looking at the little bridge far up the road. Even though it was far away, he could see it plainly. He had wonderful eyesight. He could see farther than anyone he knew.

Suddenly he showed alarm. Two riders were crossing the bridge, and he knew them. "It's the schoolmaster and that Head Man! They're coming after me on account of school. I'm going to hide!"

Israel hurried home. His busy brothers didn't see him. He ran all the way to the kitchen.

"Mother!" Israel cried. "The schoolmaster is coming, with a Salem Village Head Man!"

"You mean a selectman," Mrs. Putnam said. "He's a town officer."

"Do you think he's after me?"

"He could be. A selectman often goes with the schoolmaster when there's school trouble."

"I'll have time to hide."

"No! No! You'd just get into more trouble. You might be put in the stocks for hiding from one of the selectmen," she warned. "They are very important officers in Salem Village. Every-one must obey them."

"But we don't live in Salem Village."

"We're not far away. We have to obey the village laws."

"I'm scared, Mother!"

"S-sh! I hear the horses in the yard."

Presently there was a loud knock on the

kitchen door. Mrs. Putnam opened it, and Mr. Ezra Hopper, selectman, entered. He was followed by Thomas Riggs, the village schoolmaster. They bowed to Mrs. Putnam stiffly.

"We have come on important business," the selectman said.

Mrs. Putnam motioned to a bench. The men sat, very stiff and severe. Each held his large black felt hat in his hand.

Israel had stood when the men entered. He didn't sit until they and his mother were seated.

The schoolmaster noticed him now for the first time. "There he is!" he cried. "There's the boy who is making this trouble!"

Mr. Hopper glared at Israel for a moment. Then he spoke to Mrs. Putnam sharply. "Why did you allow this boy to stay out of school?"

"I can explain," she replied. "I——"

Mr. Hopper interrupted her. "Master Riggs, please repeat the report you gave to me."

Master Riggs took a paper from his pocket and read aloud from it. "Israel Putnam entered the school at Salem Village the day it opened, September first. He was absent the rest of that month and is still absent at this time."

"Was this known to you, Madam?" Mr. Hopper asked.

"Yes, but——"

He didn't give her time to finish. "Do you know that parents can be punished for letting a child stay out of school? It's a Massachusetts law. A man is in the stocks now for breaking it."

Again she tried to speak.

Again Mr. Hopper interrupted her. "I should hate to put you there. I know that your husband died a short time ago. You probably need this boy to help with your farm work. But I must obey the law. Have you any excuse?"

"I was afraid to send him. I was afraid he'd be captured by Indians. He saw some in the forest when he was on his way home from school the first day."

"You have no need to fear Indians," Ezra Hopper declared. "They haven't been seen around here since they sold their land to us."

"But my son saw five or six braves."

"Were they close to the road, Israel?"

"No, sir. They were back among the bushes. But I saw them."

"He has wonderful eyesight," Mrs. Putnam explained as the men shook their heads.

"I think he was mistaken," Mr. Hopper said. "Or else he made it up just to stay out of school."

"No, Israel wouldn't do that," Mrs. Putnam declared sharply.

"Anyway, he'd be safe," Mr. Hopper went on. "There are some clearings with houses between your farm and Salem Village."

"Yes, but they are far apart, with dense forest in between. Remember, it's two miles to Salem Village. And there are wolves in the forest."

"Still there is no danger. Wild beasts don't come down to the road. And Indians wouldn't dare seize him. They know we have a militia company in Salem Village. They know they'd be pursued."

"But Indians are very cunning," Mrs. Putnam argued. "They sometimes hide their captives where no white man can find them."

Ezra Hopper frowned as he stood. "It is useless to talk to you, Madam," he said angrily.

The master stood and spoke quickly, "Why couldn't his brothers bring him to school and come after him in the afternoon?"

"They can't spare the time, Master. They are behind with the farm work now."

"Then make your own plans," the selectman said sharply. "We have done our duty. Your son must be in school Monday morning."

With this, the men left. Mrs. Putnam closed the door. When she turned, she saw a troubled boy.

"Mother, I didn't make up that story about those Indians."

"I know you didn't, son. Your brothers know it, too. That's why they're clearing the hillside."

Israel was pleased. "Oh!" he exclaimed.

"But you'll have to go to school," his mother continued. "We'll have to manage it some way."

New Trouble
For Israel

EARLY Monday morning, a party of three rode horseback on the way to Salem Village. The road wasn't much more than a trail. It was so narrow the travelers had to ride single file.

William Putnam was first. Israel followed, and David came close behind. The two older brothers carried guns. All three cast sharp glances at the forest as they passed.

At last they reached Salem Village. But William stopped at the edge of town. "We're in a hurry to get back," he said. "So we won't go to the school. We'll meet you here this afternoon, Israel."

"School's out at four," Israel said.

"We'll be here. I hope the master doesn't keep you in," William teased.

A little later Israel entered the one-room schoolhouse. He hung his lunch bag on a peg in the wall. He hung his hat over it. Then he waited for the master to speak.

Presently Master Riggs turned to him and pointed to a stool. "Sit there," he said. "I'll get a bench for you later."

Israel sat down and then looked about the room. He saw just one boy he knew. This was his cousin, Daniel Hawthorn, who lived in Salem Village. The two boys were good friends.

Then school began. "The ABC class may come to the front," the master said.

Several five-year-old boys went up and stood in a row. But the master wasn't ready to begin.

"Israel, do you know your ABC's?" he asked.

"No, sir, I couldn't go to school last year on

account of the rain. The water was deep on the road in some places. No one could even ride through it," the boy explained.

"Come up front. And bring your primer."

Israel saw some of the older boys grin as he obeyed. His face grew red. He was ashamed to be in this class of babies.

"Open your primers," the master told the class. "Look at the first picture on the first page. That's the letter A. Repeat after me, A."

The class repeated, "A."

But Israel's voice was the only one heard. It was loud and heavy. It filled the room as it boomed out with "A."

Some of the pupils thought it was funny and laughed out loud.

"No laughing!" Master Riggs ordered. "I forbid it." He lifted the willow switch from his desk and held it up for a moment.

He didn't have to say more. The pupils knew

what he meant. Some knew too well. They had felt it on their backs.

The master turned to his class. "The next letter is *B*. Under it is *C*. Now go to your seats and say those letters over and over, until you know them by heart. *A B C*. Then try to find them in words in your primers."

The class went to their benches. Israel started to his stool. The master stopped him.

"I want you to read with this other class,"

he said. "Here's a book you can use. See if you can follow the other pupils."

Israel tried to follow the readers, but he could not. At last his booming voice interrupted them. "I'm all mixed up!" he cried. "I don't know which page they are on."

There were choking sounds all over the room. One boy laughed aloud. The master left his class and faced the other pupils.

"The boy who laughed may stand," he said.

No one stood.

"Who knows who it was?" he asked. "Raise your hand, please."

Not a hand was raised.

"Very well, then, I'll whip all of you. All of you, except this reading class. Now, is anyone ready to tell me who laughed?"

"I'll tell!" a frightened young boy cried.

"Good! Who was it, Johnny?"

Johnny Ray was only six, and he had reason

to be frightened. His father had told him something pretty scary this morning. "If your teacher whips you, I'll whip you again as soon as you come home."

So now the child pointed to a boy sitting near. "It was that boy."

"I'm not surprised. So, it was you, Joel!"

"I didn't either laugh out loud," Joel Jencks declared. He was a big, rough-looking boy of nine and a bully. "You can ask any of the boys," he went on. "They'll tell you I didn't."

"They'd be afraid to tell on him," thought the master. Then he spoke aloud. "We'll talk about that after school this evening, Joel. Now go on with your work, all of you."

Everyone obeyed quickly. But the minute the master's back was turned, Joel glared at Johnny.

Israel saw this look and was worried. "He'll take it out on the boy," he thought.

Now it was recess time, and the pupils went out to the school yard.

ISRAEL AND THE SCHOOL BULLY

Israel's cousin, Daniel Hawthorn, waited for him just outside the door. "Look over there."

"Yes. Is there some trouble?" asked Israel.

"Joel Jencks is threatening Johnny. I'm afraid he's going to fight him."

"He'll have to fight me first. Come on!" Israel ran toward the crowd, and Daniel followed him. Before they got there they heard Joel's voice.

"Tattle-tale! Tattle-tale!" the bully shouted angrily to the frightened little boy.

Israel pushed through the crowd to Johnny's side. "Let him alone!" he cried. "It was my fault. I shouldn't have talked out in class."

"I'll not let him alone! He's got to learn he can't tattle on me."

"He was scared. He thought he had to tell."

"I'll teach him!" Joel tried to grab the little boy's arm.

Israel pushed him away. "Don't lay your hand on that boy!"

Again Joel tried. This time Israel seized the bully and held him with his powerful hands.

"Let go of me!" Joel yelled angrily. "Let go!"

"Don't fight, Israel!" Daniel shouted. "The master will punish you. He doesn't allow fighting."

"I'm not going to fight. I tell you what I'll do, Joel. I'll wrestle you."

"All right! I'll wrestle! Let me go!"

Daniel was worried. He knew that Israel wrestled honestly and kept the rules. And he knew that Joel Jencks paid no attention to rules. "He never plays fair in any game," he thought. "I wish I could warn Israel about him."

But he couldn't, for the boys had begun to

wrestle. And then it was all over before Joel had a chance to cheat. Israel had thrown him!

The circle of boys cheered. They were delighted to see the bully on the ground. And they were surprised at Israel's strength.

Joel got to his feet slowly. His face was red with anger. "I'll pay you back!" he shouted. "I'm going to tell my brother! He's twelve years old!"

This alarmed Daniel. He knew about Joel's older brother. Just last week he'd been put in the stocks for fighting.

"I'll tell Israel," Daniel thought.

Now the master blew his whistle, and recess was over. But Israel didn't forget Johnny. He took the boy's hand and went into the school-room with him.

The master noticed this and liked Israel for it. Also he had seen the wrestling match and was glad Israel had won.

"He has courage," thought Master Riggs. "Besides, he's a kindhearted boy."

Now the master was really kindhearted himself, in spite of what he had told the selectman and in spite of his willow switch. He knew all about Joel's brother, and he was worried about Israel.

So he spoke softly to Daniel at the door. "I'd like you to take your cousin home with you at noon. I go home to dinner, you know." Then he added, "Your mother won't care, will she?"

"No indeed! She likes to have him visit us. So does my father."

"Ask him now, before I begin school."

It was hardly a minute before Daniel went to the teacher's desk. "He'll come," he said softly.

Master Riggs was pleased when he saw the two cousins leave together at noon.

"I shall go with him after school—when he goes to meet his brothers," the schoolmaster thought.

However, this wasn't necessary. Joel Jencks was absent. And Israel went off alone.

Israel
Isn't There

WILLIAM and David were on time. They had brought Israel's horse and now looked about for him. But he wasn't in sight, so they waited.

At last David grew tired. "He's had plenty of time to get here," he complained.

"Maybe the master kept him in," William suggested. "I think we'd better go to the school and find out."

The school door was locked, and no one was about. So they rode to the Hawthorn home.

"No, Israel isn't here," their cousin Daniel reported. "He wouldn't even stop to talk after school. He didn't want to keep you waiting."

"That's a lonely place where you were to meet," their uncle Benjamin Hawthorn said. "It's on the edge of a forest. There's only one house near by, and it's empty."

"Perhaps he was seized by Indians," their aunt suggested. "They may be taking him to their village. Can't you go after them?"

"We can't go into the forest now," William said. "It's dark there by this time."

"It's pitch-black," David added.

"If we don't find him pretty soon, I'll go to the captain of the Salem Village Militia," William declared. "The soldiers will march to the Indian village and demand Israel."

Mr. Hawthorn shook his head. "I doubt that they'd give him up. Israel's just the kind of boy a chief wants. He's healthy and strong. He'd make a good hunter for them when he's older."

"Oh, I hope they didn't get him!" Mrs. Hawthorn cried. "It would kill his mother."

36

"It would kill all of us," David said. His eyes filled with tears.

William also was moved. His voice trembled when he spoke. "I don't know where to begin looking for Israel."

"Perhaps the schoolmaster would know," his Aunt Deborah suggested. "He asked Daniel to bring Israel here at noon. He seemed afraid to leave him in the schoolroom."

The brothers were surprised. They turned to their cousin.

"Why was he afraid?" William asked.

"On account of Joel Jencks. He threatened Israel at recess. I guess the master thought he'd come back at noon while Mr. Riggs was at home."

"But why? Why? What had Israel done?"

Then the whole story came out. And both brothers were alarmed.

"The Jencks boys are like their father," Uncle

Benjamin declared. "He's always quarreling with someone. They've lived here six months, and Jencks has been in the stocks five times."

"We must see this Joel," William said. "Where does he live?"

"I'll take you there," his uncle replied. "But first we should see the schoolmaster. He may have seen Joel follow Israel after school."

"Let's go to the master's house at once!" William cried. "You ride Israel's horse, Uncle Ben. It will save time. You needn't saddle yours."

Mr. Hawthorn got his hat, and the riders were on their way.

"I'LL GET THE CONSTABLE!"

Thomas Riggs was mounting his horse when they rode up in front of his home. William told him about Israel, but he didn't seem surprised.

"I've been worried about the boy," he said. "I

was going now to your house, Mr. Hawthorn, to ask what you knew."

"What about Joel Jencks?" William asked. "Did you see him after school?"

"No. But it's likely he and his brother hid and waited for Israel."

"An ambush!" David exclaimed.

"Exactly," the master replied. "Let's go to the Jenckses' home and question them."

He led the way to a small clearing and stopped. "They live here in this shack," he said softly. "I'd better do the talking. Mr. Jencks will think I have the right to ask questions."

"That's true," Mr. Hawthorn agreed.

"Shall we wait here behind these tall bushes?" William asked.

"Yes. I don't want them to see you." He jumped from his horse and gave David his reins. Then he went to the shack and knocked loudly on the door.

It was opened by Mr. Jencks. He was surprised, but he didn't show it. Neither did he ask the master in.

"I'd like to see Joel, Mr. Jencks."

"What for?" growled the big man.

"I want to ask him about a new pupil, Israel Putnam. He didn't go home after school, and his family is worried."

"Why ask my son? Why would he know anything about a new boy?"

"Israel lives in the country and has to pass your house. I thought Joel might have seen him."

"He didn't tell me if he did. And he isn't here now. He's out playing with his brother."

"Where do they usually play?" asked the master.

"Oh, out in the field," replied Mr. Jencks.

"They're not there now. I looked."

"Then I don't know where they are."

Master Riggs was certain the man wasn't telling the truth. "He's trying to hide something," he said to himself as he turned to go.

Then a little girl came to the door. She was only five or so, and she didn't notice her father frown at her. "I know where they are," she said. "They went to the Witches' House."

"She doesn't know," Mr. Jencks said quickly. "She's heard the boys talking about that house. But they didn't go there. They're afraid to go near the place."

"Why? There's no one living there."

"People are afraid to move in. They say witches used to meet there at night. I guess people are afraid the witches will come back."

"Surely you don't believe those old yarns!"

"I don't know what to believe. But I wouldn't go inside that house. I'm sorry we live so close to it." Mr. Jencks pushed the child aside and began to close the door.

"We'll have to get the constable."

Mr. Jencks seemed to be frightened. But he said, "Yes, yes, by all means." Then he closed the door, and the master started away.

However, he didn't leave the yard. It was dusk now, and there were dark shadows near the house. The master went around it quickly and hid behind a large tree.

Almost at once the back door opened. Mr. Jencks came out and ran across the field.

"I knew it!" Mr. Riggs said to himself. Then he hurried to the waiting men.

THE WITCHES' HOUSE

"Did you hear?" Master Riggs asked as he mounted his horse.

"Every word. His voice sounded different after you mentioned the constable," William said. "I thought he was scared."

"I'm sure he was. He left by the back door just now. Then he cut across the field toward the Witches' House. I think his boys are there, and he's gone to warn them."

"Maybe Israel is there, too," David said.

"I believe he is," Mr. Hawthorn replied. "And those boys are forcing him to stay there. I'm going for the constable right now."

"We'll meet you at the Witches' House," said the schoolmaster.

In a few minutes the three men were tying their horses in a dark place near the old house.

"Look! There's a light in the front room," David said softly.

The men crept to the front door and listened for a moment.

"I hear voices in there—boys' voices," William whispered. "But I don't hear Israel's."

Now they heard a door close at the back of the house. Then came heavy footsteps, straight to the front room.

"Pa!" a voice exclaimed. "What are you doing over here?"

"Where's that boy?" Mr. Jencks asked. "I told you to bring him here and teach him a lesson. Did you do it? If you didn't, why didn't you? Do you want him to throw you again, Joel?"

"We did get him here, Pa," an older boy's

voice replied. "We dragged him in. We were going to beat him after supper."

"Then where is he?"

"We don't know. We locked both doors when we went to supper. When we came back he was gone," said the older boy.

"Well, you can't stay here any longer. The constable may come. Go out the back door and run across the clearing."

Presently a back door was closed, and, after that, there was silence. William tried to open the front door, but it was locked.

"Why do you want to go in?" David asked. "They said Israel wasn't there."

"He may have left some sign for us. He'd know we'd be hunting him," replied William.

"Let's try the back door," Mr. Riggs said.

The three men found it unlocked and entered. They got the candle and searched every room in the two-story house.

"Israel!" they called again and again. But there was no answer. Nor did they find any sign. At last the men gave up.

"He must have got out," Master Riggs said.

"I don't see how," William replied. "But we may as well go." He set the candle on the mantelshelf and was about to put out the flame. As he leaned over the fireplace, he heard a faint voice.

He told the others quickly. "It seemed to come down the chimney," he added. Then he called, "Israel! Is that you?"

Again he heard the faint voice. The others heard it, too, this time, for they were also listening at the fireplace. But no one could tell where the voice came from.

Suddenly Mr. Riggs remembered something. "I've heard talk of a secret room here," he said. "If it's true, it must be just above and close to the chimney. Don't you think so?"

"It must be," David declared. "The voice came down the chimney."

"Then there must be a secret stairway to it," said William, "and a secret door to that."

"We can find that out in a jiffy," Master Riggs said. "We'll thump on the walls. The sound will be different if we find a door."

Then all three began to thump.

THE SECRET ROOM

At last a different sound was heard. It was on the wall, close to the chimney, where the master was thumping. The brothers rushed to his side.

"There's a door here!" he cried. "See how it fits into the wall. Here. You'll have to look close to see it."

Yes, they saw it. But there was no knob.

"I can open it," William said. He worked on the lock with his knife. And presently the door

48

was open. The men saw nothing but black darkness as they peered through the open door.

"Israel!" David called.

"I'm up here!" Israel answered. "I can't see anything—it's dark."

Then William held the candle in the open door. It lighted a steep stairway. "Can you see now?" he called.

"Yes! I'm coming down!"

"Be careful! The steps are steep."

The boy was careful. But now he was on the last step. And now he was in the room, and they were all hugging him—even the schoolmaster.

"How did you get up there?" asked William.

"Through a closet upstairs. I found a little door, and I went into a little room. Then I closed the door so the Jencks boys couldn't find me. That made the room dark. I couldn't see a thing. I tried to open the door when you called, but I couldn't. It didn't have a knob."

"Why didn't you answer us?" William asked.

"I did, but you didn't hear me until you came to the fireplace."

"Did you know about these steps?" David asked.

"No. I was afraid to move about. I just stayed in one place."

"It was a good thing you did," the master said. "You'd have stepped off into space."

"Why didn't you try to get out through a window before you went upstairs?" David asked.

"They're all too high. I couldn't reach them."

"Made high on purpose, so the witches could fly out on their broomsticks," the master joked.

Israel laughed. "I don't believe in witches, Master Riggs."

"No Putnam does," said David.

"No Putnam ever did. Not even a long time ago," William declared.

"What was that little room for?" Israel asked.

"To hide from Indians," Master Riggs replied. "But, Israel, how did you expect to get out?"

"Oh, I knew my brothers would find me."

"We wouldn't have found you if it hadn't been for Mr. Riggs. He happened to know about the secret room," William said.

"But you heard my voice," Israel protested.

"We would have thought we imagined it— that it was only the wind in the chimney."

"That's right," David agreed.

"Israel," said William gravely, "don't ever take such a chance again. You might have starved to death in that little room."

"I didn't want the Jencks boys to beat me."

"You'd better have let them beat you. Don't ever get yourself into a trap. Learn to think ahead," advised William.

"I will the next time."

"I hope there won't be any next time," the master put in.

51

"There won't be if we can help it," William declared. "We'll bring him to the school after this. And we'll come for him when it closes."

"That would be better," Mr. Riggs agreed, "at least as long as the Jencks family lives here."

That wasn't long, however. The Jenckses left Salem Village the very next day. The constable had ordered them to leave and never return.

Israel didn't forget William's words. He thought about them on the way home, as he rode double with David. He thought about them up in the attic that night, after he went to bed.

"I don't want to get into a trap," he said to himself. "I must learn to think ahead. I must think of the bad things that could happen to me."

With this he fell asleep. And he didn't even hear the wolves howl.

Leaving the
Putnam Home

IT WAS May, 1727. A small procession crossed the bridge leading away from the Putnam farm.

A tall man led the way on a beautiful black horse. He sat straight, as an army officer might.

Just behind him rode Israel on his horse. He was nine now, but he was as large as a boy of ten. And he was as strong as most boys of eleven.

Every now and then the tall man looked around to smile at him. Israel always smiled back. They seemed to be good friends.

A two-wheeled cart drawn by two oxen was just back of Israel. It was loaded with several chests and a few bags.

On one chest sat Huldah and Mehitable. Both had to hold to the side of the cart to keep from falling off. The road was rough, and the cart bounced on its solid wooden wheels.

David, now a handsome young man of twenty, walked alongside the yoked oxen. He carried a rifle under one arm and a long staff in his right hand. He used the staff to prod the oxen and to guide them along the trail.

Once over the bridge, the leader of the little party stopped. "You'll want to look back at your old home," he said. "And this will be your last chance."

"I see William!" Israel cried. "He's still waving to us." Then he waved his hat.

His sisters and brother couldn't see William, but they waved anyway. The tall man couldn't see him, either, and he was puzzled.

"Are you sure you see William?" he asked.

David answered quickly. "He has very keen

eyesight, Captain Perley. He could always see persons crossing this bridge. He could tell who they were from as far away as our kitchen."

"Your mother didn't tell me about it. But I'm glad to know. I want to know everything about Israel. And you, too, David. I want to understand you boys, since we shall live together."

David had no chance to reply, for Israel interrupted. "There's no use to wave now," he said. "William went in the house."

He brushed the tears from his eyes. Then he spoke to Captain Perley. "How long will it take us to get to your home in Boxford?"

"If the roads aren't too muddy, we should be home before sundown. Boxford isn't really far, but we can't travel fast with these slow oxen."

"Are you sure Mother will be there?"

"Of course, Israel. It's her home now."

"It isn't likely she'd run away," David joked. "She just married you last week."

"She seemed to like her new home," the Captain said. "But she wanted her children with her. She could hardly wait until I went back for you."

"Why isn't William coming?" Mehitable asked.

"Because the Putnam farm is his now," replied Mr. Perley. "Your father left it to him when he died, and he has to live there. William's a grown man and will probably want to marry and raise a family of his own."

The child began to cry. "I'll never see him again," she sobbed.

"Indeed you will, my dear," her stepfather said. "David and Israel can take you there, when they go to visit him."

Israel's eyes were shining now. "Oh! May we go back there sometimes?"

"Whenever William asks you. You know the way. Or you will by the time we get to Boxford. Well, we'd better be moving on now."

The travelers still had to go in single file. The Captain led them along a path that had once been an Indian trail. Israel's sharp eyes were always watching the bushes on each side.

At last they reached a large clearing. Now Israel rode side by side with his stepfather and spoke with him.

"Have you had any trouble with Indians around Boxford?" he asked.

"Not for some time—two years or so."

"Are there any near your farm?"

"Not very near. There's an Indian village, but it's at least a day's journey."

"Do you ever see any braves?"

"They pass through our valley sometimes when they are hunting. They never bother us, except in one way. They do like to help themselves to one of my calves now and then."

"I'll guard the calves for you. I know how."

Now they had passed through the clearing and were again on the narrow trail. So there was no more talk.

The travelers reached Boxford before sunset. They saw the Perley farm in the pretty green valley just below them. They saw the large frame house with two stories.

"Why, it's larger than our house at Salem Village," Huldah said. "And look at the pretty green shutters at the windows, Mehitable."

But Mehitable wasn't interested in shutters. She was still gazing at the valley. "I don't see any sheep," she said.

"I don't raise sheep. I raise cattle," said Captain Perley.

"Won't I even have a little lamb to pet?"

"You'll have a better playmate than a lamb, my dear. You'll have a new sister just your age—my daughter, Margaret. And I'll give each one of you a pretty little calf to pet."

Now Mehitable was so happy she forgot all about lambs and sheep.

"I see the cattle!" Israel cried. "It's a large herd, isn't it?"

"Yes. This is a fine country for cattle. But how can you see them? I can't, from here. They're far off in a pasture."

"I can't, either," David added. "But Israel can. I believe he could see things a mile away."

"I can see the back part of the roof on your house, Captain. It has a long slope. It's almost down to the ground. At least, it looks that way."

Captain Perley was surprised. "Israel, you should be an army scout if we have another Indian war. You could see warriors far away."

"I'd like to be a scout," the boy replied. "I'd like it mighty well."

By this time the procession had reached the valley. Now they were near the Perley house.

"Halloo!" the Captain shouted. "Halloo!"

At once his new wife came from a door and ran to meet the travelers.

"Children!" she cried.

"Mother!" they called.

The Settlers
Raise a House

Now IT was November. Israel had come to love his new home, and so did his sisters and brother. They all loved their stepfather, too. He was kind to them and tried to make them happy.

There was just one thing Israel didn't like. He had no one to play with. There were no boys of his age in the neighborhood.

However, he wasn't worried about this just now. His cousin, Daniel Hawthorn, had come Friday for a short visit, and Israel was delighted.

Saturday morning Israel went out to the pasture to count the calves. He did this every Saturday. Indians might have taken one.

So Daniel had a chance to visit in the kitchen with his Aunt Elizabeth and Cousin Huldah.

"Israel doesn't talk so loudly as he did," he said. "I can notice a difference."

"His brothers teased him so much, he really tried to speak more softly," his aunt said. "William told him he'd make a wonderful army general. The soldiers would be sure to hear his orders anywhere—even on the battlefield."

"But he just laughed," Huldah put in. "And he said he'd like to be a general."

"He'd make a good one. There would be one trouble, though," Daniel joked. "The enemy would hear him, too—a mile away in their camp."

The others laughed.

"Tell us about the people in Salem Village, Dan," said Huldah.

Her cousin shook his head and stood up to go. "I think I should be out helping Israel."

"No, no!" his aunt exclaimed. "You're a visitor. Mr. Perley won't let you work. Besides, we want to talk with you. Please sit down."

Daniel smiled as he obeyed her.

Just then, Israel came in. He seemed excited about something. "Dan!" he cried. "You saw that new clearing—the one joining our farm?"

"Yes. You pointed it out to me yesterday."

"Well, the new settler is going to raise his house today. He came over to tell us."

"Has his family come?" Mrs. Perley asked. "I knew Mr. Miller went back to Boston for them."

"They came in a big cart yesterday. And there's a boy about my age, Mother. His name is Joseph."

"I'm glad to hear that. Now you'll have a playmate close by."

"The Captain and David went back with Mr. Miller," said Israel. "They're going to help raise the house."

"All the settlers around here will help. And their wives will take food for the dinner. I wish I could go, but Mehitable isn't feeling well."

"May I take Daniel over there?" Israel asked. "We won't get in the way."

"Maybe Daniel doesn't want to go."

"Oh, but I do! I like to watch a house-raising."

"Very well, but come back here at noon."

"Can't we eat there? They'll have pie and cake and everything. They always do at raisings."

"That's for the workers, Israel."

"Maybe we could help them. Couldn't we, Dan?"

"Of course we could!" Daniel liked pie and cake and everything, too.

"Well, if you boys can help, and if the Millers invite you to eat——"

She didn't need to finish. The boys had hurried out the door.

On the way, Israel told his cousin two important things. "The cellar has been dug. And the rock foundation has been laid. Mr. Miller did all that himself," he added.

"Where did he live?"

"In that hut of poles over there. He put that up, too. And he cooked over a fire outside."

The clearing was a busy place when the boys reached it. Several men were putting up the four walls of the new house.

"My goodness!" Israel exclaimed. "They have to go to the piles for their lumber. That's a waste of time. Why couldn't we carry it to them?"

Israel hurried to Mr. Miller, who was working on the front wall. "We could carry the lumber to the workers—my cousin and I," he suggested.

"That's a good idea," Mr. Miller said. "You boys will be a big help. I'll tell you when we are ready to have you begin."

"I'd like to help you," said a strange boy. "I live here. I'm Joseph Miller."

The other boys gave their names. And Israel noticed Joseph's pale face and thin arms.

"He doesn't look strong enough even to lift lumber," Israel thought. "But I hate to say so."

Then Israel's quick mind told him what to do. "Of course you can help us, Joseph. You and Daniel can take turns helping me."

"But that would make you work all the time."

"That's all right. I'm stronger than you and Dan put together. He's a town boy, like you."

"We haven't the muscles he has," Daniel said.

Mr. Miller came now and said the men were ready for lumber.

The boys worked steadily until the men stopped at noon. They were tired and hungry. But they wanted to take one look at the dinner table before they went home for lunch.

The table was just a long wide plank on the

ground. The workers were supposed to sit around it.

"You can hardly see the plank for the food," remarked Israel.

The other boys nodded. It was the truth— you couldn't see the plank.

The cakes and pies made their mouths water. So did the broiled venison, beef and mutton.

"Maybe someone will ask us," Israel told Daniel. He had whispered, but Joseph heard him.

"Of course you'll eat here," Joseph said. "Wait! I'll tell my mother."

In just two minutes he came back with a pretty little woman. "Mother," Joseph said, "this is Israel Putnam. And this is his cousin, Daniel Hawthorn, from Salem Village."

"I'm glad to meet you, boys," the smiling lady said. "I noticed how hard you were working."

"Israel and Daniel were just about to go home," Joseph said.

"Without their dinner? That will never do. Come, here's a good place to sit, opposite this baked turkey. Isn't it beautiful?"

The two boys nodded and smiled and sat on the ground by the plank. Joseph sat beside them.

"And, by the way," Mrs. Miller went on, "your mother sent this turkey, Israel. A pretty little girl brought it."

"That was my sister Huldah."

"I want her to come again. I like her."

"So do I," said Israel.

By this time the table was surrounded by the workers. "Pitch in!" Mr. Miller shouted. "Everybody help himself!" And everybody did.

CLAY FOR THE CHIMNEY

Now the men left the table, and the women took their places. The men sat under the trees, resting and talking.

Joseph took the boys to the big cart. They climbed up over one wheel and disappeared behind the high plank sides.

"Joseph wants to show them his treasures," Mrs. Miller told the women. "He has some pretty shells from the Boston beach."

At the same time the workers were talking to Mr. Miller. "We can finish the house by evening," one of them said.

"Then shouldn't we begin on the chimney now?" Mr. Miller asked. "I think there are enough rocks in that pile over there."

"Plenty," replied Samuel Moore. "I've been putting up chimneys for all these settlers. My brother Paul helps me."

"We'll need someone to bring us clay," Paul Moore remarked. "What about the boys who carried lumber this morning?"

Samuel shook his head. "Two are town boys," he said. "They wouldn't know clay from mud."

"You're right about that," Mr. Miller agreed. "I know my boy wouldn't."

"The other one should," Paul Moore suggested. "He's Israel Putnam."

"Oh! Captain Perley's stepson! He'll know. But I'll ask him, to be sure."

Israel heard Mr. Moore call him as he left the cart. "I'm coming!" he cried.

"Israel, do you know clay when you see it?"

"Of course I do. I carried clay to my brothers when they built our new chimney."

"You know where to find it, do you?"

"Yes, sir, along the creek. I know where there's a clay bank. It's close by, too."

"Then you're the boy we want," Samuel Moore said. "You can begin right now. Here, use this water bucket to carry the clay."

Israel hesitated. "What about the lumber?"

"There isn't much left. The other boys can carry it to the men."

So Israel brought clay, and the men daubed it between rocks. By suppertime the chimney was finished.

The house was finished about the same time. Then the Millers moved in. Israel and Dan helped Joseph carry some things from the cart.

Mr. and Mrs. Miller thanked the boys. "We're very grateful," they said.

"We're grateful to your good stepfather and your brother David, too," Mr. Miller said.

"And to your mother for the turkey," Mrs. Miller added. "And to your nice sister for bringing it over."

Israel and Daniel went home tired but happy. They ate another big meal, and pretty soon they were drowsy. So they went to bed early.

Daniel slept with Israel in a big feather bed. The boys were too tired to talk. In five minutes they were asleep. Not even a panther's scream could have wakened them.

Rabbits and
a Bird's Nest

THE WINTER storms began early. By the last of
November there were blizzards and bitter cold.
Snowdrifts were so deep that even town pupils
couldn't get to the school in the village of Boxford. Of course country children couldn't.

But this didn't bother the Perley family. The
Captain had been a schoolmaster once. So now
he taught the children in his own home.

Israel helped his brother and stepfather feed
the horses and cattle. And, of course, he made
his dog comfortable in a horse stall in the barn.

Some days he played with Mehitable and
Margaret when his mother and Huldah had

extra work to do. This delighted the girls, for Israel knew how to play with them. He was gentle and kind and good-humored.

Early in January, Israel was ten. There were no presents. There wasn't even a birthday cake. The church in Massachusetts didn't believe in such things.

However, the family did talk about it. The church couldn't stop that.

"Israel, I believe you're as tall as I was when I was eleven," David said.

"He's as strong as you were then," Mrs. Perley declared. She smiled at her son.

"I'm glad of it," Israel told them. "Maybe I can have a gun now."

"Not until you're eleven," his mother said.

"But, Mother, I know how to load a musket. Don't I, David?"

"He really does, Mother."

"I can stand the kick, too. Can't I, Captain?"

Mr. Perley nodded. "I let him shoot my musket yesterday. The kick didn't seem to hurt him."

"Did you fall, Israel?" his mother asked.

"Well, yes, Mother, but not very hard. I didn't mind that. I——"

His mother interrupted him. "A ten-year-old boy has no business with a gun. I don't care how strong he is. He can't think quickly enough."

"I don't see what there is to think about," Israel argued. "You see a wolf. You aim. You pull the trigger. And that's all there is to it."

"There's a good deal more than that, son. Suppose the wolf was too far away, and your bullet didn't reach it. Then, before you could reload, the whole pack would attack you."

"That's true," the Captain agreed. "It takes a long time to learn how far a bullet will go."

"There's another thing," Mrs. Perley went on. "You have to know where the animal's heart is. It won't do any good to shoot at its tail."

The Captain and David laughed, and Israel laughed with them. He was a good-natured boy, and he knew his mother was right. So that was the end of that argument.

Spring came at last. The snow had melted, and the ice was gone from the creek. Soft breezes blew, and birds began to build their nests.

But the school in Boxford didn't open. Most of the older boys had to help their fathers with the spring plowing and planting.

Israel had plenty of farm work to do. But his stepfather had told him to stop work when Joseph came over.

And Joseph had just come this morning with his new gun. "I'm eleven now," he said, "and my father gave me this musket. I wanted you to see it."

"It looks like a good gun," Israel said. "Do you know how to shoot it?"

"Father has been trying to teach me."

"Have you shot any rabbits?"

"Not yet. They get away while I'm aiming."

Israel laughed. "I'll show you how to get them. Come along! We'll go to the pasture. They're thick over there. I've killed some with rocks."

Along one edge of the pasture there were several brush piles. Israel pointed to them now.

"They're hiding in those piles," he said. "They heard our voices. I'll make them come out. Are you ready, Joseph?"

Israel kicked at a pile. At once several rabbits hopped out and ran in every direction. In a moment they had disappeared. But there was no sound of a musket shot.

"What's the matter?" Israel called. "Why didn't you shoot?"

"I didn't expect to see so many. I didn't know which one to aim at."

"You've got to think fast, Joseph. We'll try

again. Let's go down to that pile. I saw some rabbits run under it. Now then, get ready!"

Israel kicked at this pile. At once several rabbits hopped out. Again they ran in every direction. This time Joseph fired his gun.

"I got one!" he cried.

"Where is it? Did you see it fall?"

"Well—no—not exactly. But I'm sure I hit it. It ran toward that big oak tree."

"Then we'll find it," said Israel.

But there was no sign of a dead rabbit under

the oak. Joseph was ashamed. "I guess I didn't hit it after all," he said.

"I guess not." Then Israel saw something that took his mind off rabbits and muskets.

Joseph saw him staring up into the oak tree. "Maybe there's a wildcat up there," he thought. But, no, there wasn't. He looked again and didn't see anything but leaves. However, Israel was still staring up into the tree.

ISRAEL DIDN'T THINK AHEAD

"Look at that bird's nest out on that limb!"

"Oh, yes!" Joseph said. "I see it now."

"It's a new kind of nest to me. I wonder what kind of bird made it."

"I don't know. It's new to me, too."

"I'd like to see how it was made," said Israel. "I'm going up there to find out. I want to tell Huldah about it. She likes birds and nests."

79

"Do you mean to crawl out on that limb?" asked the timid Joseph.

"Of course."

"It won't hold you all the way," warned Joseph.

"I could get halfway. Then I could see the nest a lot better."

"You'd better not try, Israel. That limb is pretty high. And you might fall."

"I'm not afraid. I can tell if a limb is strong enough to hold me."

At that, he began to climb the big oak. Joseph watched with some envy. "I wish I could climb a tree like that," he said to himself.

Now Israel reached the limb with the nest. He went out on it carefully. Then he stopped, but he was still too far from the nest. So he went out a little farther.

All of a sudden the limb broke, and Israel fell. But he didn't fall all the way to the ground. His coat caught on a lower branch. He was held dangling, with his head down.

Israel tried to reach a branch with his feet, but he couldn't. He threw his arms about, but his hands couldn't even touch a branch.

Joseph leaned his gun against the tree. He tried his best to reach Israel's coat, but he couldn't. "I can't reach it!" he cried. "I'll go for your brother right away!"

"No! No! I can't wait that long. I'm dizzy. My head hurts. I can't stand it much longer."

"I don't know what to do. Tell me, Israel!"

"Get your gun and shoot at the branch that's holding my coat. And hurry!"

"I'm afraid I won't aim straight. I'm afraid I'll hit you."

"Shoot, I tell you! Shoot!"

"But what if——"

"Don't argue!" shouted Israel. "I can't stand the pain in my head. Shoot!"

Joseph's hands were trembling as he aimed his gun at the branch. He pulled back the trigger. The bullet hit the branch, and he heard a crack.

The branch broke, and Israel fell to the ground. Joseph tore the branch from the coat and then helped Israel to his feet.

Israel didn't say anything for a little while— he was too dizzy. Finally he smiled. "I'm mighty glad your father gave you a new gun," he said.

"So am I, Israel."

"I took too much of a risk."

"Indeed you did!"

"Well, anyway, I'll get the nest," Israel said.

So they hunted about till they found it. It was empty now. The boys saw broken eggshells on the ground. Israel picked up the nest.

"I'll take it to Huldah," he said. "She'll be delighted with it."

There was no more rabbit hunting that day.

The Indian
in the Barn

THE FOLLOWING week Mrs. Perley went to see Mrs. Miller. "I like your new house," she said. "This room is very pretty."

"Thank you," replied Mrs. Miller.

"I'm thankful to have a near neighbor, even if we couldn't visit last winter."

"Last winter was terrible," Mrs. Miller replied.

"But there was one good thing about it," said Mrs. Perley. "We knew there wouldn't be any Indians prowling about."

"Is it always that way in the winter?"

"Always. The Indians stay in their warm huts in their village."

"So there's no danger of an attack then?"

"None at all. It's the only time in the year when the settlers feel safe. For that reason I love winter—even if it is cold."

"It's reason enough," Mrs. Miller said. And then she added, "Is it true that warriors attack settlements in the spring?"

"It was true a long time ago, before we bought their land. No settlement has been attacked since then, however."

"But Israel saw Indians last fall, didn't he?"

"Yes, but nothing happened. They probably came to see if there were new clearings. They don't like farms. The cleared lands and plowed fields spoil their hunting."

"I'm sorry we ever came here," Mrs. Miller declared. "I'm afraid all the time."

"We're all afraid some of the time. But if I can help you in any way, I'll be glad to do so. You must come to see me. We ought to be friends."

"I shall come soon, Mrs. Perley. Joseph thinks so much of your son," she added.

"And Israel thinks a lot of your son." Then she said good-by and left.

Elizabeth Perley didn't tell her family about her call. "It's better not to talk much about Indians before the children," she thought. "We have to live here, Indians or no Indians."

That evening after supper, Israel went to the barn. He wanted to get a rope he had begun. He wanted to finish braiding it with new strips of leather to make it longer.

He wasn't gone five minutes when he came back, looking pale. "Are Mehitable and Margaret asleep?" he asked.

"Yes, sound asleep," Huldah replied.

"I've got something to tell you—all of you. But I didn't want them to hear. They'd be scared. Listen! I saw an Indian in the barn! He was in a dark corner, but I saw him."

"Israel! Are you sure?" asked Captain Perley.

"Of course I'm sure."

"Did he know you saw him?" David asked.

"I don't know. I tried to act as if I hadn't. I went to the side wall and took my rope from a peg. I took some leather strips from another peg. Then I patted my horse and left."

"Light the lantern, David," said Captain Perley. "I'll get our guns. We'll search the barn."

"May I go with you?" asked Israel.

"You stay here with your mother."

By this time the lantern was lighted. The two men went out with it and their guns.

GETTING READY FOR AN INDIAN ATTACK

"Huldah, close the door and lower the bar," Mrs. Perley ordered. "Israel, help me put up the window boards."

In a jiffy the bar was down and the boards

87

were up. Then Mrs. Perley took her gun from the mantelshelf and held it ready to use.

Huldah was frightened. "Do you think there's more than one Indian, Mother?"

"There could be. Anyway, we're ready for them."

"They could force the door," Israel suggested.

"I don't think so—it's strong. But if they do, you're not to cry, children. Even if they take all of you away, don't cry. Let the Indians think you like them. They'll treat you better."

"If they get me, I'll leave signs along the trail," Israel said. "I'll break twigs from bushes."

"That's a good idea," said his mother. "Then our settlers could follow you."

"I know what you could do, Huldah," the boy went on. "You have a ball of yarn, haven't you?"

"It's in my pocket. I was going to knit."

"Keep it there. Then if Indians get you, break off pieces and throw them into bushes you pass."

"But don't let them see you do it," her mother warned. "They might kill you."

Just then someone tried to open the door, but the heavy bar held it. At once Mrs. Perley raised her gun and stepped in front of her children.

Then someone pounded on the door. Thomas Perley's voice was heard.

"Let us in!" he called.

Israel lifted the bar and opened the door. His stepfather and David came in. Then Israel closed it quickly and lowered the bar.

"We didn't see anyone," David told them. "We looked in every corner and stall."

"Also the hayloft," Captain Perley added.

The men put their guns in a corner and set the lantern on the floor. Mrs. Perley laid her gun on the mantelshelf and turned to the men.

"I was afraid there might be several," she said. "I feared an attack."

"There's no one about," her husband declared.

"It's moonlight, too, and we could see plainly. I think you just imagined your Indian, Israel."

"He wouldn't stay there and wait for you," Israel replied. "He saw you coming with your guns."

"Well, we've scared him away," David said.

"Maybe he was an Indian spy," Israel said. "Maybe he was counting our horses."

"Well, he won't stay around," the Captain replied. "Indians don't like the way settlers shoot."

"Then we've nothing to worry about, and we can all go to bed," Mrs. Perley said.

Candles were put out. In just a little while, all was quiet in the house in the clearing.

A BIG SURPRISE

All was quiet, but everyone wasn't asleep. Israel was so worried about his horse that he couldn't sleep. "What if that Indian took him?"

At last the boy couldn't stand it any longer. "I must find out," he said to himself. "If the horses are gone, I'll come back and wake Father and David."

Israel got out of bed quietly and dressed quickly. It was dark in the bedroom, but he knew where his clothes were.

He took one stairstep at a time. But each step seemed to squeak more loudly than the last one. However, Israel reached the kitchen without waking anyone. He saw the lighted lantern and smiled. "I'm glad David forgot to put it out. I won't stumble over things."

Israel lifted the door bar carefully. Now he was outside in the moonlight. And he thought ahead this time, as he hurried to the barn. "I'll leave the barn door open, so I can get out quickly if I have to."

However, he didn't expect any trouble. He was sure the Indian had gone long ago. So he went inside with the lantern. There were the horses, each one safe in its stall.

Israel was so happy that he patted every one of them. He whispered to his own horse. "I'd hate to lose you. You're pretty!" He gave her a final pat and turned to go.

Then he saw the Indian standing in the open door! The moonlight showed him plainly.

Israel was a brave boy, but he was frightened. He couldn't run away, because he couldn't get out. He just stood and looked at the brave.

Now he had the surprise of his life. The brave began to talk. And he spoke English! "I'm glad you came back," he said. "I hoped you would. I was here when you came for your rope."

"Oh!" Israel exclaimed. He didn't say any more, because he didn't know what to say.

Then he was surprised again. The Indian came toward him, a smile on his face. And Israel saw that he wasn't a brave. He was a boy. "You needn't be afraid," he said. "I'm not an Indian. I'm white, like you."

This was Israel's third surprise. "My goodness!" he exclaimed. "You look just like an Indian boy. Your clothes——"

"Of course!" the stranger agreed. "I've lived with Indians ever since I was eight. That's when they stole me. I'm twelve now."

"How did they treat you?"

"They were good to me, and I liked them. They've been teaching me to hunt. I've liked that, too. But I was always thinking about my parents and my home. So now I've run away."

This was Israel's fourth surprise. And this time he was alarmed—not for himself, but for the runaway. "Won't they follow you?" he asked.

"They'll try mighty hard. You see, I took one of their ponies. But it was really mine. The chief gave it to me when I shot my first deer."

"But what if they track you here?"

"I don't think they can. I rode in shallow creeks halfway. They can't track prints under water."

"I'm glad of that," Israel said.

"I'd like to sleep in your hayloft tonight. I'd

be afraid to sleep in the forest—the Indians might find me."

"I'll ask Father. I don't think he'd mind."

"He wouldn't," a man's voice replied. And here was Captain Perley in the barn. "I heard you get up, Israel, and I followed you." He turned to the runaway. "I heard everything. And I noticed you didn't give your name."

"I forgot that, sir. I'm Ralph Brewer. My parents live on a farm near Boston. I'm trying to get there."

"Where's your pony?" asked the Captain.

"I hid it in the brush near by."

"Go get it and put it here in the barn. You'll find an extra stall. Feed your pony. Then we shall see about you."

"Yes, sir. Thank you." Ralph left quickly.

"We'll take him to the house, Israel. But he'll have to sleep with you."

"That's all right, Father."

"I want him where I can keep an eye on him," the Captain went on. "Maybe he told the truth, and maybe he didn't. He may be here to get information for the Indians—to find out how many horses and cattle we own."

"Then he *is* a spy?"

"I'm not sure. I said he might be. I'd like to find out before he leaves."

"I'll keep an eye on him, too," Israel said firmly. "And then I'll report to you."

Israel and the Strange Boy

THE NEXT morning, after an early breakfast, Mr. Perley and David went to the barn for their axes. The ground was too wet for plowing, so they would fell trees on the hillside.

Israel joined them. "Listen!" he said softly. "I have something to tell you about Ralph."

"Has he finished breakfast?" David asked.

"Yes, when I did. He's talking to Mother now. He told her he's afraid to go to Boston alone. He'd like to go with travelers."

"What is he afraid of?" David asked.

"Indians. He fears they will capture him on the way and take him back to their village."

"Well, that may be true," the Captain said.

"But it could be a story the chief made up for him," David added. "What else did he say?"

"Oh, that he'd like to stay with us while he waited. And that he would work for his board."

"What did Mother say to that?" David asked.

"She told him to ask you, Father."

"I'm glad she did," Captain Perley declared. "I'd like to find out whether the Indians are planning to raid our farm and steal our stock. If they are, I could tell the Boxford men who are in my militia company."

"He wouldn't tell you if he's an Indian spy," David declared.

"Of course not. But if he meets Indians in the woods, we'll know something's suspicious."

"How would we know whether he met anyone? We can't watch him while we're felling trees or working in the fields."

"I'll watch him," Israel said. "I can stop my

work any time. I'd just be trimming tree branches with my hatchet."

"That's a good idea," his stepfather agreed. "Listen for a signal—an owl hoot or a wild turkey gobble. Or it might be the call of a turtle dove."

"But I couldn't tell whether an Indian made them," Israel said.

"Ralph will know," Captain Perley replied. "You can tell by his actions. If it's a signal, he'll disappear. He'll get into the forest before you can turn around. I've noticed his motions. He's as quick as an Indian boy."

"He is just like an Indian boy. I found that out last night," Israel said. "He slept on the floor. He said my feather bed was too soft."

"Did he put on my nightshirt?"

"Yes, he did do that, David. Then he rolled up in a blanket and curled up on the floor."

"S-sh! He's coming!" David warned from the barn door, where he had been watching.

"Come on!" Mr. Perley said softly. "We'll meet him outside. Don't let on that we suspect him."

So, presently, Ralph joined the two men and Israel. "I'd like to work for you," he told the Captain. "Your wife said I might ask you."

"We're going to fell trees on the hillside. Can you handle an ax?"

"No, sir. I've never had an ax in my hand."

"Well, can you carry the brush away and put it in piles?"

"Oh, yes, I can do that!"

When the party of four reached the hill, Mr. Perley pointed to the small place he and David had cleared. "You can make piles on the right—close to the forest."

"Yes, sir," said the runaway.

"You'll get the brush from me as I cut it off," Israel told him.

"Will you cut down all of these trees?" Ralph asked David. "The hill is covered with them."

"We'll cut down most of them. We'll have a new cornfield here."

"The Indians won't like that."

"Why not? It isn't their land."

"I know it isn't," said Ralph. "But the Indians want the trees. They think they have the right to hunt here."

"Well, they haven't," the Captain said shortly. "Now then, let's get to work. There's a tree already down for you, Israel. And there's brush for you, Ralph."

In just a little while Ralph had made a big brush pile. "He could step around that and be in the forest," Israel thought.

WATCHING THE BOY

"I don't need to watch him all the time," Israel said to himself a little later. "He won't go till he gets a signal."

However, no owls hooted all morning. Neither did a turkey gobble nor a dove coo. Ralph worked steadily, and Israel was surprised.

"He doesn't seem to be expecting a signal," he thought. "He doesn't even stop to listen."

By noon, Israel saw that his stepfather was pleased with Ralph. He wondered about his mother. Would she like Ralph, too? He soon found out.

The minute they entered the kitchen, Ralph stopped and looked at the table. "It's beautiful!" he exclaimed. "So much food!"

Mrs. Perley was pleased. "Don't the Indians have plenty?" she asked.

"Plenty of meat after a hunt. But not much else. Nothing like this."

"I suppose it makes you think of your home."

"Yes, ma'am. I hope I can get there soon."

"Some settler will be going your way before too long," said Mrs. Perley.

"Not until the roads are better," Mr. Perley said. "They're knee-deep with mud now."

It was midafternoon when Israel heard an owl hoot. At once he looked at Ralph, who was carrying a load of brush. The boy stopped and listened.

The owl hooted again. Ralph hurried to a pile and threw down his brush. Then all of a sudden he disappeared.

Israel should have told his stepfather and brother. He did look at them and saw that they were busy chopping. "They didn't hear the owl," Israel decided. "I'll just follow Ralph myself."

He ran to the brush pile and around it. And now he was in the forest. But he didn't see Ralph. Israel went in deeper and looked and looked, but there wasn't a sign of the runaway. At last he gave up and went back to work.

It was a long time before Ralph joined him. "I'm ready for another load," he said.

"There isn't another load," Israel replied. "I'm tired. I'm going to rest for a while. We can sit here on this log and talk."

"This will give him a chance to explain his actions," Israel thought.

But Ralph didn't take the chance. Instead, he asked questions. "Who lives in the next clearing?" he began.

"The Miller family," Israel answered.

"Does Mr. Miller have much stock?"

"Not yet. He has a pair of oxen."

"How many horses has he?"

"Two."

"Only two?"

"That's all," Israel answered shortly. He was suspicious of Ralph now. And he became more so at Ralph's next question.

"Is there any settler around here with several horses, besides your stepfather?"

"I'll not tell him," Israel thought. So he said

he didn't know. The settlers might have sold some since he had last heard.

"Does anyone else own a large herd of cattle?" Ralph now asked.

"Why do you want to know?"

"I thought my father might like to move here. I wondered if he could buy horses and cattle from these settlers."

"Oh, I see!"

But Israel didn't see. "It's just a good excuse," he thought. "I'll tell the Captain what Ralph said." Israel did tell him that evening, in the barn.

"It could be the truth," his stepfather said. "And it could be a story. I'm not sure yet. But there's one thing I am sure about: I don't want you to follow Ralph into the forest again. Do you understand me, son?"

"Yes, sir. But you were busy and——"

"You should have called me anyway. Suppose

you had found him with an Indian. What would you have done then?"

"I hadn't thought of that."

"A fine general you'd make! Your troops would say you never figured out anything until the battle began. And then it was too late."

Mr. Perley went on, "The next time Ralph disappears, come to me. I'll follow him, but I'll have my gun."

"I'll tell you—I promise. Oh! About being a general—don't you think I could learn to plan ahead?" asked the boy.

"I hope so. If you don't, you won't even make a good farmer."

THE BRANCH AND THE BOY

Another week had passed, and nothing more had happened. Israel had begun to think a good deal of Ralph Brewer. Joseph liked him, too.

"I like his Indian stories," Joseph had just told Israel.

"So do I. Everyone at home likes them, too."

"Even Mehitable and Margaret?"

"They're the worst of all. They never want him to stop. I can't believe that Ralph's a spy."

"Neither can I, Israel. Do you still watch him when you work?"

"Hardly ever. I forget to."

"You'd remember if you heard a signal."

"I haven't heard an owl for a long time. Not since he first came here."

"I guess the real owls have left this part of the forest," said Joseph.

"I guess so," agreed Israel.

Then one day an owl hooted close by!

Israel saw Ralph standing by the brush pile, listening! Then the owl hooted again. Another owl seemed to answer. "They're talking to each other. They *are* Indians!" Israel thought.

The boy knew that his stepfather and David had not heard. Their tree had begun to crack. It was about to fall.

And Ralph had disappeared! That settled it. Ralph had gone to meet those Indians.

Then Israel lost his head completely. He forgot his promise to Mr. Perley. The next thing he knew he was in the forest. He didn't see Ralph, but he heard voices. So he hid behind a bush.

Now he heard the voices again. They came from those big rocks just ahead. So the fearless boy crept nearer and nearer, but he was careful to keep behind the bushes.

At last Israel reached the rocks. He heard the voices plainly now on the other side. "Ralph must be with them," he thought. But he wasn't sure. So he planned a way to find out.

"I could get up on that boulder and peep over. No, I can't do that. They might see me."

Then he had a new idea. He broke a large leafy branch from a bush and held it in front of him. Then he began to crawl out on a big rock.

"The Indians will think the bush grew here between the rocks," he thought.

Suddenly Israel's feet were seized by strong

hands, and he was pulled back to the ground. He looked around. It was Ralph!

The runaway seized the branch and threw it down angrily. Then he grabbed Israel's arm.

"Come!" he whispered. "Don't let them see you. We'd better make a run for it."

In just a little while they were back in the clearing, and Ralph was explaining to the men. "I heard the owl hoots. I knew they were made by Indians."

"Were they signals to you?" the Captain asked.

"No! No! To other braves who had become separated from them. I was afraid they would see me in this clearing. So I hid in the woods."

"I don't blame you for that," David said.

"I had to hide once before. That was my first day here. I didn't see those braves, but I thought they were after me."

"I'm glad they didn't find you," Israel said.

110

"I am, too. But I was scared today. Four braves passed the bush where I was hiding."

"Why did they come?" the Captain asked. "Did you hear their talk?"

"They came to count the new clearings."

"Then we needn't fear a raid on our stock?"

"They didn't speak of a raid," Ralph replied.

"I almost saw them," Israel said.

"You—what?" Captain Perley asked.

Then the rest of the story was told. And the stepfather turned to Israel and spoke sharply.

"Do you know that Ralph saved you from capture? Those Indians would have known that the branch didn't belong on the boulder."

"Of course," Ralph agreed. "They'd laugh at a bush or branch moving forward."

"I didn't think they'd notice."

"They notice everything. Indians are smart."

"Oh, dear!" Israel exclaimed. "I'll never learn to plan things right."

"I think you will," his stepfather said kindly. "You're learning now—from all of these mistakes. By the time you're a general, you won't make them," he teased.

"Me, a general?" Israel exclaimed. Then he laughed. But he was pleased and happy when he went back to work a few minutes later.

The Wolf Hunt

THE SUMMER SUN had dried the wet earth some time ago. Fields had been plowed at the Perley farm, and crops had been planted.

Israel and Ralph helped with all of it. Today there was no work for them, so they sat under a tree in the yard and talked.

Pretty soon Joseph came. He sat down beside them and listened. He heard the boys say that they were glad the rains were over and the crops had a good chance to grow.

Then Ralph added, "There can't be any more mud on the roads now. This one is dry."

"All of them are," Joseph told them. "My

father said so. He asked about it in Boxford yesterday. Maybe someone will be going to Boston soon."

"I should think someone would be going," said Ralph. "Haven't you heard of anyone?"

The boys shook their heads.

Then Ralph added: "It's time I was going home."

"I don't want you to leave," Israel said. And he meant it. Ralph was part of the family now.

"Do you think the Indians will find you, Ralph?" Joseph asked. "I mean, if you stay much longer."

"I'm sure they know where I am now. Their scouts are always prowling about."

"Here?" Joseph looked scared as he asked.

"Certainly. They watch settlers all the time."

"We never see them."

"It isn't likely you ever will. They hide in the brush and watch."

114

"Why don't they capture you?"

"I never go into the forest alone, Joseph—not any more."

"And my brother and stepfather always have their guns," Israel said.

"But if a whole band of braves came——"

"They're not ready for a fight or they would," replied Ralph. "Maybe they've used all their bullets and powder. Or they're out of arrowheads. But as soon as they're ready, they'll be here. That's another reason I want to get away. I don't want any of your family hurt, Israel."

"Captain Perley doesn't think they'll come for you. There'd be a fight. And Indians don't like to lose a single brave," he said.

"They don't want to lose a hunter, either," said Ralph. "There must be meat enough for an entire village of men, women and children. And I helped to get it for them."

"Can't their warriors hunt?" Joseph asked.

115

"They're always fighting other tribes. They have little time for hunting."

Just then Israel's dog, Boots, came and went at once to Ralph.

"There!" Israel exclaimed with a smile. "Look how Boots goes to you."

Ralph petted the dog. Then he got up. "I must put my pony in the pasture to graze."

Ralph left, and, almost at once, Joseph rose to leave. "I have to go now," he said. "I have to help Father. I just came over for a little while."

"Come along, Boots!" Israel said. "We'll take him part way home."

GOOD-BYS AND A SAD BOY

That afternoon Joseph came back with his father. It was just after dinner, so they came straight to the kitchen.

116

"I wanted to see all of you," Mr. Miller said as soon as he and Joseph were seated. "We came to say good-by. We're going back to our old home."

"I'm sorry to hear that," Mrs. Perley said. "You have been good neighbors."

"No more frontier life for me. I've had enough, and so has my wife. We're scared to death of an Indian attack. And I can't work with a gun in my hands," Mr. Miller said.

"Lean it against a tree near by," David suggested. "That's what we do."

"But think of the things that could happen if I were on the other side of the field. Plenty of arrows could be shot while I was crossing to get my gun."

No one answered that. No one could. Everybody knew it was true.

Finally Mrs. Perley spoke. "You've done a lot of hard work. It's a shame to lose your home."

"I don't care! My wife doesn't care, either. All I want is to be safe in my old cooper shop in Boston."

"Boston!" Ralph cried as he sprang to his feet. "That's where I want to go. May I ride behind your cart?" he asked.

"You may ride in it, Ralph. You can hitch your pony to the cart. And you'd better come tonight. We're starting at dawn tomorrow."

"We'll pack the cart this afternoon," Joseph added quickly.

"I'll help you," Ralph said. "I'll go back with you now."

"Good!" Mr. Miller exclaimed. "Then get your pony now. You won't need to come back here."

Now good-bys were said, and then the visitors and Ralph left.

Captain Perley and David weren't working today, either. So they stayed in the kitchen and talked about the good neighbor they'd lost. And they said how much they thought of Ralph.

Only Israel was silent. He felt so bad he couldn't say anything. So he went outside.

"What's the matter with him, Mother?" Huldah asked. "I've never seen him act like this."

"He's upset about Joseph and Ralph. He feels lost and lonely."

"Daniel will cheer him up when he comes back this summer," David suggested.

"But he won't be back till fall, and then only for a visit," Mrs. Perley said.

"I know a way to cure his loneliness," Captain Perley said. "Let's give him a gun."

"A gun? Now?"

"Yes, Elizabeth, now. We'll take him hunting. That will give him something new to think about."

"But he isn't eleven yet!"

"He's so close it doesn't matter. Besides, a

frontier boy must learn to shoot as soon as possible. He must protect himself against many dangers."

"Israel could help William get rid of wolves," David suggested. "He asked me to help. He sent me a message."

"A very good idea," the Captain said. "But Israel must learn to use a gun first."

"Well, then, I consent," Mrs. Perley said.

"Good!" the Captain cried. "We'll go to town at once. Come along, David."

At the same time, Israel had stopped to pat his dog. He didn't say anything—he couldn't— he was afraid he'd cry. He just kept on patting.

Suddenly Boots turned and looked at the boy's face earnestly. Then he followed Israel to a stump and sat by him quietly.

Every now and then Boots touched Israel's hand with his nose. And once he licked his face.

"I believe he knows I feel bad," Israel thought.

"He's trying to show me he understands. I wonder if he knows that Joseph and Ralph have gone for good." Then he spoke out loud. "You do understand, don't you, Boots?"

The dog barked sharply twice and looked with sad eyes at the lonely boy.

HE TALKED, LAUGHED AND SANG

Israel didn't see David and Mr. Perley ride away. He had gone to the far cow pasture.

Huldah found him there. "Israel!" she called. "Supper's ready!"

121

"I don't want anything to eat."

"Come on! There's a surprise for you."

"Is it a cake?"

Huldah shook her head and giggled.

"A pie?"

Again Huldah shook her head and giggled. "I won't tell you. But it's nice."

"All right, then, I'll come."

As soon as he entered the kitchen, Captain Perley gave Israel a package. It was long and was wrapped with cloth. "It's a present for you from all of us," the Captain told him.

"For me!" Israel exclaimed. "Why, it's a gun! Did you change your mind, Mother?"

"I decided we didn't need to wait till you were eleven. You're almost that."

"Unwrap it!" David cried. "Or shall I do it for you?" David reached for the package.

"No, no! I'll do it!" Israel took off the cloth and held the gun in his hands.

"It's beautiful!" he cried. "It's the most beautiful gun I ever saw. I thank all of you."

"Oh! I almost forgot to give you your ammunition," David said, handing Israel another package.

"Bullets," Israel said as he took it. "Thanks for them, too."

"And here's your own powder horn," said the Captain, handing the horn to him.

"Now you can kill rabbits," Huldah said.

"Yes, and you can kill wolves, too," said his brother. "You can go with me to see William. You can help us."

The others now took their places at the supper table. Israel leaned his gun in a corner carefully and joined them.

Israel was a different boy. He talked, laughed and smiled. He even started to sing. Mehitable tried to sing with him. But the two made so much noise Mrs. Perley had to stop them.

"The Indians will run when they see me and my gun," Israel boasted. "So will the wolves."

"Everything will run if you don't learn to shoot straight," David teased.

"I'll learn," Israel said seriously.

"Sing some more," Mehitable said.

"More!" little Margaret cried.

"No!" cried several voices.

THE MUSKET KICKED TOO HARD

A week later David and Israel were at William Putnam's farm near Salem Village. David had put up a target. It was a square piece of thin wood fastened to a tree trunk. In the center of the square was a brown circle, made with walnut juice.

"You must hit the target inside the circle," David explained. "When you can do that, you'll be ready to aim at an animal."

"And kill it quickly, instead of just wounding it," William added.

"I'll show you how to load," David offered.

"I know how. I've watched you and William, and Captain Perley, too."

The gun was loaded. Now Israel made his first shot at the target. Instantly he had the surprise of his life. The gun kicked so hard he fell against David. David fell against William, and then all three were on the ground.

They all laughed. But as soon as Israel got to his feet, he tried again. He had better luck this time. He only staggered when the musket kicked. But his bullet missed the target.

However, within one week he didn't stagger at all, and he was hitting dead center every now and then. Israel's brothers weren't surprised. "It's his wonderful eyesight," they said.

"Keep that up, and you can go on the wolf hunt with us," William told him.

The following week, Israel hit center almost every time. So one morning the three brothers set out with their guns. They found fresh wolf tracks by the sheepfold. They followed them to a pile of rocks on the hillside. Here the tracks ended. This told a story to the older hunters.

"A wolf came to these rocks today," William remarked. "The tracks here are fresh. And they all point toward the rocks. There isn't one leading away. There could be a cave in there."

"I'll crawl in and see," Israel said. He was about to start, but William held him back.

"Suppose you did find a cave, would you enter it, Israel?"

"Of course!"

"Even if you knew there was a wolf inside?"

"I wouldn't be afraid. I'd shoot it."

"You're too daring. The wolf would spring before you could lift your gun."

"But you said I was quick with my musket."

126

"Not as quick as a wolf. Besides it would be dark inside the cave. You couldn't see a thing."

"I could see its eyes shine," Israel insisted.

"I'll shine you if you ever try such a thing," William said firmly.

"And I'll help you," David said.

"We might as well go back," William suggested. "If there is a wolf in there, it won't come out now. It has heard our voices."

David nodded and followed William. Israel followed David, but he didn't want to leave. "I'm disappointed," he said.

"That's all right," William told him. "You're still alive, aren't you?"

"Yes, but——"

"There aren't any 'buts.' You'll keep out of caves when I'm around."

"We have to get the wolves, don't we? They've killed a lot of your sheep."

"They have," David agreed, "and just for the

fun of it. Fifty in one night and only three eaten!"

"We'll get them when they come to the sheepfold," William said. "We'll watch tonight."

It was moonlight when the three hunters went to the fold. They spoke softly to the sheep. Then they hid behind thick bushes near by.

At last three wolves came out of the woods. They ran toward the fold in single file.

William whispered, "The first one, Israel. The second, David. I'll take the third. Wait till they come closer. I'll say when."

Each hunter aimed his gun and waited.

"Now!" William cried.

Three Putnams fired. Three wolves dropped.

"My first wolf!" Israel cried proudly.

"It was a good shot, Israel," William said, "a very good shot, for the animal was running."

"Well, they won't be having any fun tonight," Israel declared.

Boats and
Beavers

Israel's cousin Daniel came home from school in the early fall. He had come on a sailboat from Boston. It had taken three days!

"We should have been here in three hours," he told his parents. "But there wasn't any wind, so we just sat and waited."

Two days later he was telling this to his relatives on the Perley Farm in Boxford. And soon after, Israel was asking him questions about sailboats.

He asked so many, Daniel couldn't begin to answer them. "Come with me, Israel," he said. "I'll take you down to the docks in Salem, and

130

you can ask a sailor. He could answer your questions better than I could anyway."

"Israel ought to know about boats. We're only a few miles from the ocean," the Captain added.

So a few days later the two boys were on a dock at Salem. Israel was talking with a sailor.

"Where is that boat going?" the boy asked. He pointed to a boat that had just sailed.

"She's bound for England," the sailor replied.

"But that's clear across the Atlantic Ocean!"

The sailor smiled. "She can make it. Why, we have boats sailing farther than that. That one leaves for Spain tomorrow, if there's a good wind."

"My goodness! And where will that one go— that small boat?" asked Israel.

"To New York. We've room for just one more passenger. Want to go?"

"I wish I could. But I haven't any money."

"You could work for your passage. You'd make a good sailor—you're strong."

"Maybe, when I'm older——"

"Fine!" the sailor put in. "I'll be expecting you in a few years," he joked.

"Is there a boat from Boston?" Daniel asked.

"There's no passenger ship. There's a cargo boat. She's tied up at the next dock. She brought in a load of fish this morning."

"Could I take my cousin over to see her?" asked Daniel. "I just want him to see a Boston boat."

"Certainly, go right along. Kind of proud of Boston, aren't you? Do you live there?"

"No, sir. I go to school there. And much obliged for everything."

The boys found the cargo boat easily. It was rather small, but it was shining with fresh paint.

"It isn't built like the passenger ships," Israel said. "I'd like a closer look."

"Let's go aboard! There's no one around to stop us. Come on!"

The boys went aboard, but Israel stopped suddenly and pointed to a sailor on the deck. The sailor's back was to the boys, and he was busy with a fish net. He hadn't even heard them.

"What's the matter with you?" Daniel whispered. "You needn't be afraid of him."

The sailor turned. He had heard a voice.

"Ralph!" Israel cried.

"Israel!" the sailor shouted.

The next hour was a happy one for the two friends. Daniel enjoyed it also as he listened to their questions and answers. His Aunt Elizabeth had written him about Ralph several times.

"It's my father's boat," Ralph explained. "I'm learning the cargo business."

"Do you like it?" Israel asked.

"I like it better than being an Indian."

The others laughed. Then Ralph took them into the tiny cabin for dinner. He fried a fish he had caught. The boys said it was delicious.

Then they said good-by and left. All the way to the Hawthorns' home in Salem Village, the boys talked about their adventure. And think of meeting Ralph again! They hadn't expected that. Why, it was wonderful!

"Won't my folks be surprised!" Israel exclaimed. "I must go back tomorrow, Daniel. I want to tell them right away."

"I don't blame you, but I hate to see you go so soon, Israel."

But Israel went anyway.

ISRAEL'S BEAVER STORY

Israel's stepfather didn't hold school in his home in the fall. So Israel went to school in Boxford. Four new boys from new houses in new clearings went with him. They didn't have horses, so Israel walked with them.

But now winter had come with fierce winds and deep snow. The school had closed. The new boys stayed at home by their fires, and Israel did the same.

Sometimes he made up stories for Mehitable and Margaret. This evening he told them a beaver story. And the others listened, too.

"Once I went on a long hunt. I expected to be gone all winter, so I built a hut to live in."

"I thought you lived here," Margaret said.

"He does," Huldah told her. "He's just pretending he was hunting."

Then Israel went on: "My hut was on the bank of a little lake. But I wasn't alone. A family of beavers lived in this lake. The old beavers were building a dam at one end, and their children were playing in the water.

"I loved to watch all of them. Mr. and Mrs. Beaver carried logs to the dam, and——"

Mehitable interrupted. "In their arms?"

"No, they pushed them somehow as they swam along. Then somehow they daubed mud between the logs. Pretty smart, wasn't it?"

"Yes," Huldah replied. "It was smart. But why did they do it?"

"To make the lake deeper. The dam held the water back—didn't let it drain out."

"Oh, yes!"

Israel went on: "I loved to watch the young

beavers swim and dive. And I thought their danger signal was wonderful."

"Oh!" Huldah cried. "Did they give signals?"

"They certainly did, every time they heard an odd or strange noise. They would beat the water with their broad flat tails. Then every beaver would dive and disappear instantly."

"Could they all hear the signal?"

"Yes, indeed! It made plenty of noise. I could hear it in my hut."

"What were the beavers afraid of?"

"Panthers and bears and wildcats."

"Weren't they afraid of you?" asked Mehitable.

"Not after a week or so. Why, one of them would swim along the shore beside me as I walked around the lake."

"Was it a young beaver?" asked Margaret.

"Yes, Margaret, it was. And one day it warned me. It gave me the danger signal.

"I had shot a deer and had hung it inside my hut. 'I'll skin it tomorrow,' I said to myself. 'I'm too tired now.'

"I sat on the bank to rest. Presently here came my young beaver friend, swimming fast. He stopped just below me and began to beat the water with his tail. But I didn't know the signal was for me."

"Was it?" Mehitable asked quickly.

"It was. I found that out right away. I heard a noise in the brush behind me. I jumped up and looked around. Here came a panther! And I didn't have my gun! I'd left it in the hut!"

The two young girls were excited.

Israel went on: "The panther had smelled the deer I had killed, and it was going toward my cabin. So I tried to get there first to get my gun. I didn't want to lose my game."

"Did you get there before the panther did?" Huldah asked.

138

"I just did, and that's all. I almost shut the door on its nose."

Captain Perley and David laughed.

Israel paid no attention to them. He went on with his story. "I fastened the door quickly. And I was glad that I had a strong bar, for the panther began to push against the door."

Mehitable and Margaret were frightened now. "Did it get in?" one asked.

"Oh!" the children cried. "Oh!"

Their mother looked at them closely. Then she put down her knitting and sat between them and held their hands.

Israel continued: "Now the beast seemed to leap at the door. Its claws scratched the wood. I was afraid it would get the deer and me, too."

"Oh! Oh!" the sisters cried. Both were so frightened they trembled.

"That will be enough, Israel," Mrs. Perley said sharply. "You've scared them."

"I didn't mean to scare them. I just got started and couldn't stop."

"Well, this is a fine place to stop. The panther didn't get in, girls. It finally went away," Mrs. Perley said.

"I'm sorry I scared you, girls," Israel said. "There wasn't any panther. I just made it all up for fun," he added.

"Fun!" his stepfather cried. "Why, I was afraid myself." Then he began to laugh.

"So was I," David said. "I was sure the door wouldn't hold." And he began to laugh.

And pretty soon the others were laughing also.

In just a few minutes, Israel was popping corn over the fire. Soon they were all eating it, warm and happy around the fireplace.

Crows and
Indians

Warm spring weather brought more and more settlers and their families. Almost every day some came to this beautiful Massachusetts country.

Axes flashed in the sun. Trees fell down, and houses went up. It was that way from the Perley Farm to the village of Boxford.

The Perleys were delighted to have so many neighbors. There was less danger of an Indian attack.

"The warriors won't dare to fight us," the Captain declared. "There are far too many settlers living here now."

But the arrival of these new settlers meant more work for the Captain, David and Israel. They always helped to raise the new houses and barns.

"I don't have to carry the clay any more," Israel told his mother. "They let me build chimneys now. And next week, they're going to let me do siding and roofing, too."

"Good! It won't hurt you to know how to put up a house. You may have to do it sometime when no one's around to show you."

The Putnam boys and their stepfather helped others so much that their farm work was neglected. At last, however, they were plowing their fields and planting their corn.

But again their work was stopped, not by new settlers but by crows!

"It's a battle all day long," Israel said one evening. "David plows a furrow, I plant the corn seed, and the crows dig it up and eat it."

"Then we plant seed again," David added. "And again the crows eat it."

"Don't they fly when you shout at them?" asked Mrs. Perley.

"Oh, we shouted until we were hoarse," Israel replied. "They'd fly away, but they'd come right back again—and come back laughing."

"Crows can't laugh," Margaret said.

"It sounds like laughter to me," said Israel.

"They have a right to laugh," David said. "They are ahead of us so far. A whole day of work and not a seed in the ground."

"There are so many of them, too," the Captain remarked. "If any more come, they might chase us off the field."

"Have you tried a scarecrow?" Mrs. Perley asked.

"Yes, but it didn't scare them away. The crows roosted on its arms and sat on its head."

"You can't scare a crow," Israel declared. "I

wonder who made up that word? Scarecrow! Humph!"

No one spoke. There was silence for a moment. Then Mrs. Perley said, "I'm sorry, but I think you will have to shoot them. We can't afford to lose our corn crop. We'd have no corn meal for bread."

"Or mush," Huldah added.

"We'll take our guns with us tomorrow," the Captain said. "We'll have to kill them. There's no other way. We must get the corn in."

There were no crows laughing when the firing began the next morning. After a few had dropped to the ground, the others flew away. They didn't return, either.

So the corn crop was saved. And the Perleys were sure of having cornbread and mush for another year at least.

ISRAEL SINGS FOR FRIENDS

It wasn't all work for Israel. He had fun, too. After an early supper, he would join the boys in the neighborhood for games.

There were a dozen or more new boys living near by now. And everyone of them liked Israel.

"He's a good-natured boy," they told their parents. "He never gets mad. If a game goes wrong, Israel just smiles, and we try again."

"You ought to see him run," another boy told his father. "I think he could race with a deer."

"I think he could wrestle with a bear," still another boy declared. "And he would win, too."

But an older boy told his parents that Israel Putnam was a strange lad. "He won't take a dare like the other boys. I dared him to jump from a boulder the other day, but he wouldn't."

"He must have known how high it was," the mother remarked.

"No, he didn't know. I didn't tell him where the boulder was. There are a lot of them around. He said he'd have to see the rock first."

"That was smart," the father said. "He wasn't taking any chances. Remember, Israel's a frontier boy. He knew he might have broken his leg."

"The other boys would have jumped."

"Then they're the strange ones—not Israel. That lad thinks ahead. I like him for it."

"So do I," the mother agreed.

"Oh, we all like him," the boy said.

Soon after this the new boys found another reason for liking Israel. They had met at the Perley farm this time. But it began to rain, and this stopped their games for a while.

Mrs. Perley invited them into the house. Some sat on benches and stools. Others sat on the floor.

But no one knew what to do. The boys didn't know what to talk about. There was a long silence.

Finally Mrs. Perley said, "Get Israel to sing."

"Yes! Yes!" the boys cried.

"I don't know what to sing," Israel said.

"What about your school songs?" she asked.

"Yes! Yes ! Yes!" the boys cried.

So Israel stood up and sang:

> "Oh, teacher dear, I'm sorry
>   I can neither write nor spell.
> But I can read a line, by jing!
>   'The cow jumped in the well.'"

The boys clapped their hands and laughed.
"Go on! Go on!" they cried.

> "Oh, teacher dear, I see your whip,
>   And I'm ready for your whack.
> Three pairs of pants are on my legs,
>   Six shirts are on my back."

"Ha! Ha!" the boys laughed. "Sing it again!"

Israel sang both verses again and again. The third time the boys sang with him.

Then Mrs. Perley and Huldah brought hot corn meal cakes and milk and honey.

The rain had stopped now, and the boys went home. They sang Israel's song on the way.

"INDIANS! LEAVE AT ONCE!"

One morning that spring, the Perleys were eating breakfast. Only the young girls were still asleep. It was very early, before dawn. So it was still dark, and several candles were burning.

Suddenly everyone stopped eating. A horse had come close to the house. Now a saddle squeaked.

Everyone was surprised. No one ever came this early. But before anyone had time to speak, there was a loud rap on the door.

Mr. Perley hurried to open it. And again the family was surprised. They saw a stranger. His hard-ridden horse was tied to a bush outside the kitchen door. What could this mean?

"Bad news!" the stranger cried. "Indians attacked the new settlement on the river last night. They burned every house and barn."

Now the others were at the door.

"Will there be an attack here?"

"I'm afraid so. The Indians are angry about so many new clearings and settlements. I think you ought to go to Boxford at once. I'll warn your neighbors."

With that the stranger rode away quickly.

Then the old soldier, Captain Perley, took charge of things.

"Elizabeth, put out the cook fire. David, you and Israel saddle our horses. We'll be ready by the time you bring them. Hurry! I must get to Boxford and tell the militia."

Everyone moved quickly. The Captain turned to Huldah. "Wake your sisters."

"They'll cry."

"Pay no attention. Bring them, if you have to carry them. Hurry!"

Huldah hurried to the bedroom. Mrs. Perley put out the fire, and Mr. Perley put out the candles. Now Huldah came with the girls.

By this time the horses were at the door. Captain Perley helped his wife mount. Then he put Mehitable in front of her.

Huldah mounted by herself. David put Margaret in front of her. Then he rushed into the house for their guns and powder horns.

He came back with three. "Here's yours, Captain. And here's yours——" He was about to say "Israel." But the boy wasn't on his horse, "Where is he?" the older brother asked.

The others didn't know. They had supposed he was here, on his horse.

"Israel!" Captain Perley called. "Israel!"

There was no answer.

"Go on!" the Captain told his wife.

"We can't go without him," Mrs. Perley cried.

"You must, Elizabeth. Do you want the warriors to capture you and the girls?"

"No! No!"

"Then go now, at once. And ride fast. Go to the church at Boxford. I'll find Israel. We'll be close behind you on the road. Give me his gun and powder horn, David."

The Captain switched his wife's horse, and it started off running. Huldah and Margaret followed, but David didn't know what to do.

"Shall I help hunt Israel?" he asked.

"No! Go with the rest of the family. You may have to protect them on the way."

David mounted and rode after the others. One hand held his bridle. In the other was his gun.

Thomas Perley went through the house. "Israel!" he called. "Israel!" But there was no answer.

The Captain was puzzled. "Israel knew we were going to leave," he thought. "He heard me tell him to bring the horses. And he did."

Then the Captain went outside, but he didn't know what to do. He didn't dare to stay here much longer But he couldn't bear to leave without Israel.

He began to think of the things that might have happened. "Israel might not have heard the messenger say he would warn our neighbors. He might have gone to the nearest house himself. He thought he'd get back by the time we were ready to go. If he did that, he might have been captured by Indian scouts."

"Israel!" he called again.

Now the boy answered, "I'm coming!" And he ran from the barn with his dog in his arms.

The stepfather ran to meet him. "What do you mean?" he cried angrily. "Did you expect us to wait for you till the warriors came?"

"I didn't want them to get Boots."

"Well, hurry to your horse. Put the dog down. He'll follow us."

"He can't," argued the boy. "His paw is sore."

"Put him down anyway! Now then, jump into your saddle. I'll hand you your gun."

"I can hold Boots in front of me. He's used to riding that way with me."

"All right. I'll lift him up. Hurry, Israel!"

Israel jumped on his horse. The Captain put the dog in front of the boy and gave Israel his gun.

"I don't know how you'll manage all of that," the stepfather said as he mounted his horse. "You must be ready to use your gun. We might meet Indians on the way to Boxford."

"Oh, I'll manage. Boots will hold to the saddle blanket. Won't you, boy?"

Then man and boy rode hard and fast till they arrived in Boxford. There they heard good news. Captain Perley's lieutenant had gathered the militia. They were ready to start now against the Indians.

"I must join my troops at once," said the Captain when he heard the news. With that, he rode off.

The next day the militia, led by Captain Perley, rode up to the church in Boxford. The settlers who had been hiding in the church came out to hear the news. It was good news, too.

The warriors had been driven back to their own country. So there would be peace for a time at least. The settlers whooped and cheered.

After the celebration they went back to their farms—the Perleys with them. And very soon those young farmers were working in their fields.

"It's just as if nothing had happened," Israel said to his stepfather.

"That's the way it is on the frontier," Captain Perley replied. "You never know what to expect."

"Just so it isn't Indians," David said.

"Or crows," Israel added with a smile.

Too Many Deer

It WAS a rainy day in late May. Woodcutters couldn't work in the forest. Farmers couldn't go into their fields. It was a good time to visit.

Two farmers had just come to see Captain Perley with their two young sons. The men, Mr. Little and Mr. Apple, were near neighbors.

The boys had wanted to come, because they were friends of Israel. They had said they didn't mind the rain. Now, however, they hated to go into the Perley house, because their clothes were so wet. Their fathers felt the same way.

"Oh, don't mind that," Mrs. Perley told them. "Come right in. You can dry out by the fire."

"Yes, indeed!" Captain Perley said. "Here take this bench by the fireplace."

Presently, wet clothes were drying fast. Steam was rising from coats, trousers and shoes.

"I expect you think we're foolish to come out in this rain," Mr. Little began.

"Foolish or not, it had to be done," Mr. Apple declared. "We've got to decide something, Captain. We wanted your advice."

"If I can be of any help, I'll be glad——"

Mr. Apple interrupted. "You wouldn't be helping us alone. You'd be helping yourself, too."

"It's about the deer, Captain," Mr. Little explained. "There are more deer this year than ever before. They've become a pest."

"I agree with you," the Captain replied. "They eat the corn sprouts as soon as they're out of the ground. They're as bad as crows."

"They're eating our vegetables as soon as they

come up," Mrs. Perley complained. "Young beets, cabbages, potatoes, beans and radishes, all eaten or crushed by their hoofs."

"Ours, too," Mr. Little growled. "I'm afraid we won't have a vegetable to put in our cellar for the winter if we don't stop them."

"I'm afraid every cellar in this neighborhood will be empty," the Captain said gravely.

"But we must have vegetables!" Mrs. Perley cried. "We can't get along without them. We'd all be sick. We'd have scurvy."

"Would it kill us, Pa?" Thomas Apple asked.

"No, but it might as well. We'd all be so sick we couldn't work. We'd lose our teeth, too."

"That's true," Mrs. Perley said. "I've seen it happen in families that ate nothing but meat."

The boys were alarmed and showed it.

"I don't want to lose my teeth," Israel said.

"Neither do I!" cried Thomas and John.

"We'll have neither crops nor vegetables if

we don't get rid of dozens," said Mr. Little. "Shooting a few won't do any good."

"No, we've tried that," Mr. Apple agreed. "Have you any plan, Captain Perley?"

The Captain didn't answer. He stared into the fire.

Mr. Apple spoke louder. "We thought you'd suggest something. You make plans for the militia."

Everyone looked at the Captain and waited for him to speak. But he didn't. He just sat and stared into the fire.

WILL THEIR MOTHERS CONSENT?

At last the Captain spoke. "I was thinking of large hunting parties. Then several men would shoot at a deer herd at the same time. There would be no waiting for guns to be reloaded."

"Every farmer in this county will be glad to

go," Mr. Little declared. "They're all worried about their crops and gardens."

"Each group should have five or six men," the Captain went on. "And they should hunt for a week. When they returned, another group would go out. Then another and another until the deer disappear."

"That's a splendid idea!" Mr. Little cried. "Will you take charge of the groups, Captain?"

"I'll be glad to, and I'll go out with one."

"Put me down for one," Mr. Apple said.

"Put me down," Mr. Little said.

"Me, too!" David exclaimed.

The three young boys had been whispering together. Now Israel spoke. "Can't you put us down, Father—John, Thomas and me?"

Captain Perley looked at his wife. Israel noticed this and knew what it meant. So he spoke again. "We know how to handle guns. We've all been out hunting."

"Not alone. At least you haven't," his mother said. "You've always been with your brother or father."

"So has Thomas," Mr. Apple said.

"And so has John," Mr. Little said.

"Indian boys go into the forest alone when they are twelve," Israel argued. "I'm twelve and four months. John is thirteen and Thomas is fourteen."

"You're all too young unless you go with an older person. And all of the men will be in their own groups."

"I could go with them, Mother," David offered.

"I was counting on you to form a group of young men," the Captain said.

"Well, then, Israel, you see how it is."

"We don't need anyone, David. We can go alone for a few days—while the men are getting ready to leave."

"My boy can't go unless his mother consents," Mr. Little said.

"Neither can mine," Mr. Apple declared.

The rain had almost stopped now. There was only a drizzle. So the visitors left. But the men would come again, they said, whenever the Captain wanted them to help him get the groups of hunters.

After they had gone, David asked Israel to help him mend a harness in the barn.

As they worked, David talked. "This will give Father a chance to talk to Mother about your hunt."

"Do you think he'll let me go?"

"Yes indeed! And he'll try to get her consent."

"Oh, I hope so!"

"Father thinks frontier boys are men when they're thirteen years old.

"I'm larger and stronger than John and Thomas. I could carry John on my back."

162

"I believe you could, Israel. And Father knows that, too. He's proud of you."

"I'm glad——"

"The other men will try to persuade their wives, too. I could tell by the way they smiled when you said all three of you wanted to go. They both were pleased, and so was Father."

"Wouldn't it be wonderful if all our mothers consented?" Israel said.

"It would, if you really want to go."

"Of course I do! I never wanted anything so much in my life."

THREE YOUNG HUNTERS

The mothers had consented. And now, the day after, the three young hunters had started on their deer hunt. Each carried a gun. From each belt hung a powder horn and a long knife in a sheath.

Each carried a blanket, a bag of corn meal, a gourd cup and a bag of cornbread and parched corn.

Israel had an extra bundle. In it were a long-handled skillet and a gourd bowl, full of grease.

He smiled as he thought about the grease. "I won't need this," he had told his mother.

"Your cornbread won't last long," his mother had replied. "Then you'll have to eat meal cakes. How will you fry them without grease?"

"They'd stick to your skillet," Huldah had said. "You'd tear them to pieces trying to get them out."

"I'll take the grease," Israel had said.

Now Thomas spoke as the boys trudged along. "Mother wanted me to bring some salt pork. But I told her we'd find our own meat. We'd get game on the way."

"That's what I told my mother!" John exclaimed. "I said we'd find plenty of rabbits."

"But we expect to eat deer meat tomorrow," Israel added quickly.

His friends laughed.

"I'm not joking. Father said we'd be sure to find deer at the swamp. They like the tender plants that grow there. So that's the place we're bound for."

This was all right with the others. They expected Israel to manage things. He always managed their games. They only said they hoped he knew the way.

"Of course I do. My folks told me. And I promised to go straight there, and not to go deep into the forest, either."

"Shall we get there today, Israel?"

"We could. But David said not to camp near the swamp—too many mosquitoes. They'd eat us up."

Around ten, the boys sat on a log to rest. They had been walking since dawn and were tired.

But they had their guns ready to shoot. They might see a deer at any minute.

But they didn't. So after a while they went on. At noon they stopped again. This time they got rid of blankets, bundles and guns.

They were too hungry to scare up rabbits and skin and cook them. So they ate cold cornbread and parched corn from their food bags.

Their dessert was a cold drink from a spring near by. Then, after they had rested, they took up their things and went on.

In an hour or so Israel said they must look for a place to camp. "It gets dark early in the woods."

"Indeed it does," Thomas agreed. "By four o'clock."

Israel continued. "I want to find David's old camp. He said there was a big sycamore on the bank of a wide brook. It's only about one mile from the swamp."

It was a good two hours before they found the
tree. The young hunters made camp at once.
Blankets, bags and bundles were thrown on the
ground. Guns were leaned against the tree.

Then the boys hunted rabbits, but with rocks
for weapons. They didn't want to waste their
powder. In no time at all, each hunter came
back with one.

These frontier boys knew what to do with
them, too. They skinned and cleaned them.
Then they put them on pointed sticks and held
them over the small fire they had built.

When the rabbits were brown, the boys ate them with their cold cornbread. Each one bragged about his own.

"Why don't you sing for us, Israel?" Thomas asked. "Sing one of your funny songs."

Israel shook his head. "It's late, and we must get up early, at sunrise."

Then they wrapped up in their blankets and slept on the ground near the dying campfire.

The boys rose at dawn and ate breakfast. Then they went to the brook for a drink.

GOOD AND BAD LUCK

Now the hunters started to the swamp. They had a long walk but finally got there. And they were disappointed. There was such heavy fog they couldn't see each other unless they were close together.

"There aren't any deer here," Israel said.

"Let's cross the swamp. They might be on the other side."

"I won't go into that swamp till the fog lifts," Thomas declared. "Why, you couldn't see a snake until it moved its head to strike."

"I'm sure I could see one in time," Israel said. "Remember my eyesight."

"That's right," John replied. "I'll follow you."

"I'll wait here," Thomas said.

In another moment the boys had disappeared in the fog. Before long there was the sound of gunfire.

Pretty soon Israel came back. "I got one deer!" he cried. "The others ran before I could reload."

"Why didn't John shoot?"

"I don't know. I wondered about that."

"But he was with you!"

"No, he wasn't. We were separated somehow in the fog. He might not have seen the deer."

"I wish he'd come. I'm tired of fighting mosquitoes. I want to get away from this place."

"So do I. My goodness! These mosquitoes are as big as grasshoppers. It will be a battle as long as we're here." After a while Israel stood. "John has been gone too long. I'm going after him."

"Into that swamp?" Thomas asked.

"Yes. He followed me—he must be in there."

Thomas went with him to the edge. "I ought to go with you, Israel, but honestly, I'm afraid."

"That's all right. You stay here and watch for deer. You might get one. And, for goodness sake, don't shoot across the swamp," he joked.

Thomas heard him calling John's name several times. He thought he heard another voice, but he wasn't sure. Then there was silence.

Before long, he heard Israel's voice again. This time it seemed nearer. In a little while Israel came out of the swamp, carrying John on his back!

"He sprained his ankle and couldn't walk," Israel explained. Then he gently lowered John to a log.

"We'll get you back to camp," Thomas said.

"I don't see how I can get there. It's too far for Israel to carry me, and I know you can't, Tom."

"We'll make a crutch for you," Israel said. "I'll get a strong tree branch with a fork. We'll cut it the right length for you. And there you are! You'll walk to camp, Johnny."

And that's the way it was managed. Thomas went back for John's father. Horses were brought, and the three hunters rode home.

"Hunting isn't all fun," Israel told David that night in their room.

"I'm glad you found it out. It's work, brother, and hard work at that."

Fearless Ranger

ONE SUNNY spring day in 1756, three soldiers sat under a tree in the town of Pomfret, Connecticut. The Indian War was still being fought, and these men had been in it. But they had been wounded and had come home to get well.

Now another wounded soldier joined them. He was waving a letter and smiling. "I thought I'd find you here," he cried. "I've got news for you! I've just received a letter from Israel Putnam!"

"Oh!" the others exclaimed. And they smiled.

"Sit down here, Sergeant, and tell us what he wrote you," one man said.

"Well, he wrote he had good health and hadn't been wounded yet."

"He's lucky," a soldier said. "He's been in the Indian War more than one year now."

"That's right," another agreed. "He was among the first to go when Connecticut called for volunteers."

"He'd have been with the Massachusetts troops if he hadn't moved here after he married," the third soldier said.

"Well, anyway, Connecticut was lucky to get him," the sergeant declared. "Israel's a very brave man."

"He's a good soldier, too," the eldest man said. "And we ought to know. We were all in his company after he was made a lieutenant."

"Certainly we know," the third agreed. "He never complained about the long, rough marches in the forest, or the poor food, or maybe none at all."

174

"Never!" voices cried.

"He was always more worried about us than he was about himself," a man declared.

Now the sergeant waved his letter again. "He wrote some other good news. Israel's been promoted to captain!"

"Captain!" the others exclaimed. And they began to smile proudly.

"He's to command a company of rangers," the sergeant added.

"Rangers!" the others cried. The smiles faded from their faces. Not one was pleased.

"That's dangerous work," the eldest soldier declared. "It means spying on the enemy. And that means getting close enough to their camps to count their warriors."

"That takes mighty brave men. They are likely to be discovered and captured," another added.

"I don't see how they could escape," still another said. "There are guards around every camp, day and night."

"But spying has to be done," the sergeant insisted. "Our general should know how many warriors he'll have to fight. But it's a risky job."

"Israel was never afraid to take risks," the eldest said. "But he never rushed into danger with his eyes shut. He planned every move he made."

"Yes," another agreed, "he was a great one to think ahead. He said he had to learn to do that."

"Well, he learned," the sergeant declared. "There never was a better lieutenant. Here, read his letter. Israel said it was for all of us."

ESCAPE THROUGH THE RAPIDS

Several months later, more news was brought to Pomfret by a young ranger. He had a fever and had come home to get well. He belonged to Captain Putnam's company.

The ranger told the wounded soldiers that Captain Putnam had made a good ranger. "One of his duties was to patrol the forest near the enemy camps with his company. And you know how dangerous that was."

The eldest nodded. "I do. Warriors would be hiding, just waiting for them to come. That's the way Indians fight. They always try to surprise their enemy."

"But they didn't surprise the Captain, did they?" asked a younger soldier.

"No, indeed they didn't," the ranger replied. "He seemed to know when the Indians were about. And he nearly always got us back to camp safe and sound. He usually had valuable information for the general, too—the number of warriors and guns."

"If anyone could get it, Israel could," the sergeant said. "But there's one thing I don't understand. Why did his men follow him into such danger? They weren't forced to go. Spy work is voluntary."

"Because Israel treated them so well—as if they were his friends. And every one of them knew he would always try to rescue them from danger—if it meant his own life."

"He would, too!" put in the eldest. "Once he carried a wounded man from the forest. It was a wonder that the Indians didn't get him."

The ranger went on: "There was one time when he barely made it. He was in a small boat on a river with five rangers. Suddenly a large band of Indians appeared on the shore and pursued them.

"There was only one way to escape the arrows," the ranger continued. "That was to take the boat through the swift rapids and great rocks just below. And that's what the Captain tried to do."

"He took a great risk," a soldier put in. "The

boat could have been thrown against the rocks and crushed like an egg shell."

"That almost happened. Time and again the rapid current whirled the boat toward the rocks. But the Captain always steered it away. Once he even turned the boat completely around to avoid the great rocks."

There were exclamations of surprise from the others.

"The Indians were amazed at his skill in steer-

ing," the ranger continued. "They were also amazed at his success. No one had ever gone through these rapids before, but Putnam did."

"Didn't the Indians shoot at the soldiers?"

"Yes, but not an arrow hit them. The boat moved too swiftly. And finally, they reached smooth water and got away."

"Putnam was always lucky," said one man.

"It wasn't luck," the eldest told him. "He knew how to handle all kinds of small boats. He had learned when he was a boy—when he visited his cousin in Salem Village. The two boys spent their days on the seacoast, sailing and rowing."

"There's always a reason for everything," the ranger said.

THE FIRE—THE CAPTURE

The following year another wounded ranger told the story about the fire at Fort Edwards on the Hudson River. "Putnam and his company were living in the fort at this time," he explained.

The Pomfret soldiers nodded.

"Well, a fire broke out inside the fort. The flames were near a powder magazine when the fire was discovered. There would be an explosion if it reached the powder. The fort would be blown up—all the men in it."

"Of course!" the soldiers exclaimed.

The ranger went on. "Captain Putnam knew this. But, in spite of the danger, he mounted a ladder near the magazine. He ordered his men to bring buckets of water. Then he poured water on the flames until they died out."

"Was he burned?" a soldier asked quickly.

"Yes, badly. It was some time before he recovered. And then, before he could join his men, he was promoted again. Captain Putnam became Major Putnam."

The Pomfret people heard the story about the

fire. And so did farmers for miles around. They were all proud of Major Putnam's bravery and hoped he would come home soon to rest.

So hardly anyone could believe the bad news when it came the next month.

Major Putnam had been captured by a large force of warriors! The Indians had treated him cruelly and were about to kill him. But a French officer had saved his life.

The American officers were thankful. The soldiers and Israel's many friends were delighted. And, of course, his family was happy.

At last the long war was over. The Indians had been defeated, and there was peace. Then Israel went home to his family in Connecticut.

General Israel Putnam

It was 1775. Israel Putnam now owned one thousand acres of good land near Pomfret. He was making money, for he worked hard. He had just recently built a large, new house for his family. The house was well-furnished, and they were comfortable and happy.

One day Israel was plowing a field that bordered on the highway. Two strong horses pulled the plow, and Israel guided it. His next to youngest son, Daniel, drove the horses, which were hitched tandem—that is, one behind the other.

Suddenly a rider came galloping along the

highway. He stopped at the field and called out to the workers: "There's news! Bad news! British troops attacked the militia at Lexington, Massachusetts. The Governor of Connecticut wants volunteers."

"I'll volunteer!" Israel Putnam cried as the messenger galloped away. "I'll enlist at once!"

Mr. Putnam turned to his son. "Daniel, get someone to finish plowing this field. I'm going to the stable for my horse. I hope you'll follow me into the army. We'll need every good man we can get."

The patriot army was very glad to get the old Indian fighter. Thousands of Indians fought on the British side, and the American generals didn't know much about fighting them. They needed advice.

"Putnam should know their tricks," one general suggested. "He has already fought them for seven years."

"He was a bold ranger," another general added. "There's no one who would know more about the redskins than Israel Putnam."

"That's true," still another general agreed. "I've heard many stories about his bravery in that Indian War. It was said he could smell an Indian ambush."

The others laughed as they separated. But that very day they began to ask Putnam's advice.

So Israel soon became an important officer in the patriot army. In fact, he was so important that he was made a general himself.

His son, Daniel, was now a soldier in his father's regiment. So was his eldest son, Israel, who was his father's aide.

Early in the War of the Revolution, at the Battle of Bunker Hill, General Putnam became a hero.

"Powder is scarce," he told his men. "You must not waste it. You are all good marksmen.

You could kill a squirrel at a hundred yards. So, hold your fire until the enemy is so close you can't miss."

Israel's troops obeyed him. They waited till the British were close. Then they fired and drove the enemy back.

The men under General Putnam talked about this battle afterward.

"I never saw a braver officer," one man said. "He was out in front all the time."

"Yes," another said, "the British bullets flew around him, but he didn't seem to mind."

"He seemed to be fearless," added another.

As the war went on, more and more persons came to think of Israel as a fearless man. And one of these was General George Washington.

"General Putnam's courage is remarkable," he told a friend. "He is always eager for action. He is never unhappy over the hardships of a soldier's life. And his troops seem devoted to him."

"They are," replied the friend. "His cheerfulness gives them courage."

STORIES ABOUT PUTNAM'S BRAVERY

Both of General Putnam's sons were proud of him. The older son, Israel, wrote to his mother: "Father is a great favorite in the army. Men are proud to belong to his regiment."

The younger son, Daniel, also wrote her: "We try to have fun here in camp sometimes. Maybe the regiment will have a dinner. But the men think they can't have it without Father. They say he is jolly and good-natured. They like the funny stories he tells and the funny songs he sings.

"In fact, they won't let him off without a song. Then the men want another and another. Father's voice can be heard all over camp. But that's all right. It makes everyone feel happier."

His soldiers liked to talk about Putnam. They liked to tell stories about his bravery.

A Pomfret soldier had just begun one. And the other soldiers in his tent were listening.

"I knew Israel Putnam was brave before he even went to the Indian War," the man said. "I had a farm near his, just out of Pomfret. I went on a wolf hunt with him and some other farmers.

"All of us had lost sheep. Night after night they had been killed. Seventy of them in just one night."

"There must have been a whole pack of wolves," a soldier interrupted. "And all of them hungry."

The Pomfret man shook his head. "No, we studied the tracks. There was one set, and it was the killer's. That wolf didn't kill because it was hungry, either. Only one sheep had been eaten.

"So we took our guns and followed the wolf's

tracks to a dark cave among big rocks. Since the hounds wouldn't go in, Israel decided he would. We told him it would be too dangerous."

"Of course!" several voices exclaimed.

The soldier went on: "But Israel wouldn't listen to us. So we tied a rope around his waist, and then he crawled into the cave. He carried a torch in one hand and his gun in the other.

"Then he saw the wolf's eyes shining at the back of the cave, and he heard its fierce growl. It was ready to spring. But Israel shot it before it had a chance. He was just that quick with a gun."

"Wonderful!" the men cried.

"I heard he wanted to go into a wolf's den when he was a boy on his brother's farm near Salem Village," a young soldier said. "But his brothers wouldn't let him."

"That is true," the Pomfret soldier replied. "Israel once told me about it."

189

"I can believe it," a corporal spoke up. "Of course he was a fearless boy. He had to be, to make the kind of man he is now."

The war went on. General Putnam and his troops fought in battle after battle. In every one he showed his marvelous courage. And he had many narrow escapes from the enemy.

One day General Putnam and a small body of troops were out on patrol. Suddenly they met a large force of British soldiers. The General ordered his men to hide in a swamp where the British couldn't follow. For himself he chose a dangerous means of escape.

He was now at the top of a hill. It was so steep it was almost like a wall of rock.

Steps had been cut into the rock wall for foot travelers to the valley below. Putnam didn't hesitate a moment. He rode his horse down those steps—seventy steep stone steps—at breakneck speed!

The enemy didn't dare to follow. They fired at him, but their bullets whizzed past. One went through his military hat.

When the General reached the valley, he turned in his saddle and waved his sword. Then he galloped away to safety.

The British commander was amazed at General Putnam's daring escape. He even sent him a new hat to replace the one ruined by a British bullet.

At last the war was ended. The American army had won. The British troops went back to England. And General Israel Putnam was safe with his family on their Connecticut farm.

His many friends came to see him. Many strangers came, too. Everyone was proud of him.

"There's no better patriot in America," they said. "And there's no more honest man nor braver soldier."